G000167759

T175 NETWORKED LI

Exploring Informati
and Communication Technologies

Block 2
Communication and identity
Part 3

Prepared on behalf of the course team
by Judith Williams

This publication forms part of an Open University course T175 *Networked living: exploring information and communication technologies*. Details of this and other Open University courses can be obtained from the Student Registration and Enquiry Service, The Open University, PO Box 197, Milton Keynes MK7 6BJ, United Kingdom: tel. +44 (0)870 333 4340, email general-enquiries@open.ac.uk

Alternatively, you may visit the Open University website at http://www.open.ac.uk where you can learn more about the wide range of courses and packs offered at all levels by The Open University.

To purchase a selection of Open University course materials visit http://www.ouw.co.uk, or contact Open University Worldwide, Michael Young Building, Walton Hall, Milton Keynes MK7 6AA, United Kingdom for a brochure. tel. +44 (0)1908 858785; fax +44 (0)1908 858787; e-mail ouwenq@open.ac.uk

The Open University
Walton Hall, Milton Keynes
MK7 6AA

First published 2005. Second edition 2007.

Edited and designed by The Open University.

Typeset in Europe by the Alden Group, Oxford.

Printed and bound in the United Kingdom by Halstan Printing Group, Amersham.

ISBN 978 0 7492 1526 2

2.1

Course Team List

Karen Kear, course team chair

Ernie Taylor, course manager

Patricia Telford, course secretary

Academic staff

Mustafa Ali

Chris Bissell

David Chapman

Geoff Einon

Clem Herman

Allan Jones

Roger Jones

John Monk

Nicky Moss

Elaine Thomas

Mirabelle Walker

Judith Williams

John Woodthorpe

Media production staff

Geoff Austin

Deirdre Bethune

Annette Booz

Sophia Braybrooke

Sarah Crompton

Jamie Daniels

Vicky Eves

Alison George

Mark Kesby

Lynn Short

External assessor

Prof. Philip Witting, University of Glamorgan

Contents

Part 3
Device to device

Judith Williams

Study Session 1: Communication between devices

1.1 Introduction to Part 3

The two previous parts of this Block have looked at communication systems where people are the main players – either communicating with each other, or retrieving information from computer systems. This part looks at communication systems where *devices* are the main players, passing information to and from each other and possibly acting on that information to produce some kind of outcome. In these interactions, people may not be involved at all, or may have roles that are limited only to the initial setting of schedules (such as when certain tasks should be performed) and parameters (such as particular conditions that should be satisfied before a task is performed). Some people may see this as liberating – relieving humans from the tedious tasks of everyday living. Some may see it as threatening – taking control away from humans and placing it with computers and machines.

How do devices 'talk' to each other? What technologies and processes are involved? What kind of world does it create? These topics, and others, will be explored in the study sessions that follow.

In this and the following study session I shall give a general introduction to communicating devices and some basic principles of how they communicate.

In Study Sessions 3–5 I shall look at wired and wireless communication technologies, introducing you to some of the key methods currently in use. I shall also look at some of the issues influencing the choice of network technology.

The final three study sessions (6–8) build on these foundations by looking at two particular systems where devices communicate with one another: 'smart' homes and a system of electronic identity tags known as RFID.

Throughout there will be opportunities for you to develop and build your skills, particularly in relation to reading, numeracy and study. Study Session 8 also provides an opportunity for you to review a particular aspect of your learning.

1.2 Communicating devices

Your introduction to communicating devices starts with an article from a technical journal – the sort that is read by academics and professionals working in a related technical field. This sets the scene for some of the technologies and issues that you will be encountering later in this part.

I'm not going to ask you to read the entire article, but I would like you to get an idea of the article's contents, the kind of points the author is making, and the range of issues that it throws up. With this aim in mind, I'm going to lead you through a method of getting an overview of the contents of a document without actually having to read it through completely.

When reading any document there are some good reasons for starting off by getting a quick overview. If you are looking for some specific information, an overview enables you to assess whether the document contains anything that is of use to you. (There's no point spending more time ploughing through it only to find it doesn't hold what you were looking for.) If it does, you might choose to concentrate only on the section that is of interest to you. On the other hand, if you are reading the document because you want to assimilate its entire contents then an overview gives you a familiarity with the document before you engage with it in depth. This will be easier if you know the direction in which you're heading (it's easier to navigate on a journey you've travelled before). An overview will help you to identify particular parts you may really need to focus on.

1.2.1   Skimming to get an overview

A well-structured document usually contains a number of clues about its contents. Skimming is the practice of finding and using these clues. These are:

- visual clues such as a document's title, headings, subheadings, figures and figure captions; words in boldface and italics; and numbered and bulleted lists;

- verbal clues such as the introduction and conclusion or summary, and the first (or sometimes the last) sentence in each paragraph.

Specialised documents often include a brief abstract that summarises the main points of the text. The abstract is usually presented before the main text, followed, in some cases, by a list of keywords or phrases. These provide some helpful pointers to the core points and ideas of a text. When authors write articles for professional journals they are usually asked to provide an abstract and some keywords even if these aren't to be included with the article itself. The reason for this is that the abstract and keywords can be listed in the search results when library catalogues are searched.

I'll shortly be asking you to skim an article which appeared in the Spring 2003 issue of a journal called *IEEE Technology and Society Magazine*. 'IEEE' is usually referred to as 'i-triple-e' and stands for 'Institute of Electrical and Electronics Engineers' – a professional

association based in the USA. The article can be accessed through the OU Library. It's not long (five pages) but it does include a highly graphical front page which makes it a very large electronic file. For this reason I am not going to ask you to download it. Instead it is supplied in print in Appendix 2 at the end of this part.

If you were to access this article through the OU Library you would also have the opportunity to read the abstract and key words that I talked about earlier. Instead this abstract has been reproduced in Appendix 1 at the end of this part. However, if you would like to try your hand at finding the abstract for yourself next time you are logged on to the internet, then go to the OU Library site, click on 'electronic journals' and follow the instructions given for accessing an article in a particular publication.

Activity 1 (exploratory)

Go to Appendix 1 at the end of this part and read the abstract and keywords (labelled 'index terms') to the article *Networked microsensors and the end of the world as we know it*. What do you expect the article to be about?

Comment

When I read the abstract, I expected the article to discuss some quite radical and unsettling future changes in the way we live our lives. The article's title includes some very emotive words: 'the end of the world as we know it', and the abstract talks about changing society significantly. I assumed these changes would involve the use of computers − perhaps in a way they are not currently used − because the abstract talks about bringing people 'into closer contact with computers'. In the list of keywords (called 'index terms' in this example) I could see the terms 'microsensors', 'networked sensors' and 'automation' so I suspected the article would be something about devices that sense physical states (such as temperature or pressure) or events (such as a particular change in physical state) and relay the information to computers. I thought perhaps this sensing and relaying of data might be done automatically, and/or the process might trigger some automatic response.

To me, it seemed clear from the abstract that the author would be looking at four main areas − manufacturing, military operations, personal health and personal freedom.

Activity 2 (exploratory)

Now turn to the copy of the article printed in Appendix 2 and look for any of the visual clues I listed earlier that could provide you with more information about the document's contents.

Comment

The article uses only five sub-headings. These appear to be related to the four main areas identified in the abstract, plus what I assumed would be a concluding section ('Pros and cons abound'). I couldn't see a sub-heading relating directly to personal health, but I assumed that this would be discussed in the section headed 'Biological applications'. There aren't any figures to provide further clues.

I could see only a few instances of italicised words but these didn't help me much, and there are no numbered or bulleted lists. On the second page there is a box of large type which confirmed, rather than added to, the impression I'd gained from the abstract.

Activity 3 (exploratory)

Now read all of the introduction, which consists of the two first paragraphs of the article, and the conclusion, which consists of the whole of the final section 'Pros and cons abound'. What additional insights to the article's contents has this given you?

Comment

My impression from reading the introduction and conclusion was that the article would focus on future applications where miniature devices and increasingly powerful computers are linked into networks to monitor and control aspects of our environment. While identifying many of the advantages this can bring to society, I thought the article would also raise concerns about potential state control and loss of personal privacy that the use of such systems may bring.

Whilst reading the introduction and conclusion you may have noticed some numbers included in the text. Some were shown as superscripts (small figures or characters raised above the normal line of text) and others in square brackets.

Each superscript gives a cross-reference to an endnote listed at the end of the article. These notes give additional information that could interrupt the smooth flow of the document if they had been directly incorporated into the text.

Each number in square brackets gives an index to a reference list at the end of the document. This reference list gives details of all the original sources of information that the author has directly referred to or quoted from in the text. Another common and often preferred method of indicating an original source is to substitute the bracketed index number for a short reference consisting only of the author's surname and the year of publication of the article – for example, (Allgood, 2001) instead of [1] in the Shepherd article – and then to list all the information in alphabetical order of authors' surnames in the reference list.

Another, very important, reason for getting an overview of a document is that it will help you to avoid taking a passive approach when you read the document in full. A passive reading approach is one where the reader puts in very little effort. The outcome of this sort of reading tends (at best) to be a string of unconnected facts and ideas in the reader's mind, with very little coherence or structure. At worst, it can be a complete blank, where the reader has gone through the motion of reading but has actually drifted off to think of other things.

An active reading approach involves reading in a disciplined manner with some purpose, and thinking continually about what you are reading. As you skim a text, questions will probably occur to you – for example, 'What is the author trying to say here?'; 'What is the evidence for this?'; 'Do I agree?'; 'How do I feel about this?'; 'What more do I need to know?' Seeking answers to questions like these gives focus to your reading.

Activity 4 (exploratory)

Working from your understanding of the article, how do you think the topics it raises might have an impact on you? What questions do you hope the article will answer? What authority do you think the author has for giving his opinions?

Comment

Here are my reactions to those questions.

The four main areas the author will be discussing could each have an impact on my life, but 'personal health' and 'personal freedom' sound as though they will have a more direct effect on me. I feel intrigued but slightly anxious. I think that the health effects are likely to be beneficial (possibly providing earlier detection of health problems and faster, better treatment when they arise) but I do feel concerned about privacy and control. Might I have to relinquish some of my freedoms in order to gain benefits? What might these be and what is the pay-off? I notice that the article appeared in Spring 2003 and I wonder how the world has moved on since then. I wonder if the article predicts any changes that have already started to happen.

The IEEE is a reputable professional organisation so I expect that the article would have been reviewed by other professionals in the field. This leads me to feel pretty confident about the authority of the author.

As I said earlier, I'm not going to ask you to read through the whole of the article – though of course you may if you wish. (Perhaps you are keen to see if it answers any of the questions you identified in Activity 4.) Instead I would like you to return only to the first two paragraphs because these give a useful introduction to the idea of devices 'talking' to each other. The rather futuristic view presented in this section introduces you to some of the things involved when devices communicate and take actions. It identifies elements that interact with each other to perform some function.

Activity 5 (exploratory)

What are all the elements mentioned in the first two paragraphs that enable devices to function together as an ICT system? Is there anything else you can think of that would be needed?

Comment

The extract identifies sensors, actuators, computers (processors), storage devices, and databases. But it says nothing directly about what connects all these together – the communication link – and what rules are needed to enable the devices to talk to each other.

I would like you now to think about a simple ICT process you are already familiar with – the process that starts when you click the Print icon on your computer's word-processor screen. For now, imagine that there is simply a point-to-point connection between your computer and

the printer (as indeed there may well be) and that the printer is not being shared with other computers. So here there are two devices – your computer and your printer – each communicating with the other. The printer itself is controlled by a processor and it has memory, so you can think of it as an additional computing element. In order to 'talk' to each other, your computer and printer need some kind of communication link between them. They need protocols (rules) to establish a common language and to control the exchange of data (what to say and when to 'speak'). At a more sophisticated level they might also need some way of storing data (for example, what is known as a 'print queue') and some way of recognizing and coping with errors.

Figure 1 shows a block diagram representing the computer/printer system. The communication link is point-to-point so there is no requirement for network routing, or for storing or manipulating the data as it travels through the communication link. The computer receives the print command from the user and sends data over the communication link to the printer. The paper copy produced by the printer is an output to the user.

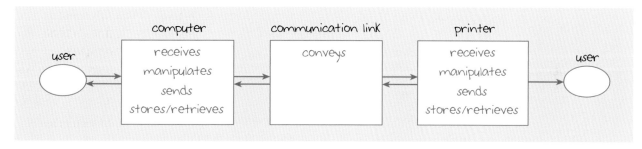

Figure 1   Representation of a point-to-point communication between computer and printer

It's likely that the data will need to be held in a **buffer** – a dedicated portion of the printer's memory – before being processed. Notice how all but one of the arrows between the elements in Figure 1 are shown in two directions. This indicates a communication path from the printer to the computer as well as from the computer to the printer. For example, at some point the buffer may become full and the printer will need to signal to the computer to stop sending data for a while. The final output from the printer is in one direction only.

buffer

Figure 2 expands the arrangement of Figure 1 to show a representation of a network where two computers share the services of a printer. Notice how there may now be a need for routing, storing and manipulating data as it travels through the communication links. (This is indicated by the lighter-shaded text in the network box.)

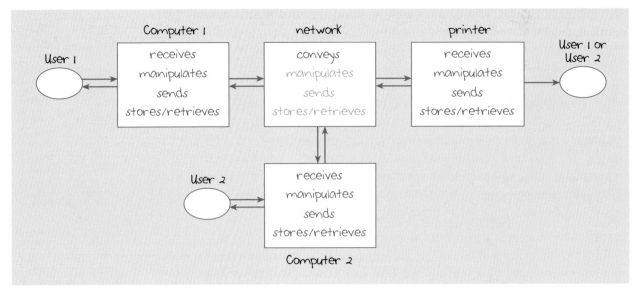

Figure 2   Representation of a computer network

Activity 6 (exploratory)

Think about the additional complications of receiving and sending the necessary data between the three devices shown in Figure 2. What is needed to avoid confusion?

Comment

In order for two computers to share one printer, it is important to be able to identify each device so that data can be correctly directed to the intended destination. Protocols are needed to establish how the printer will be shared so that one user doesn't 'hog' the resource, and to establish some way of sharing the communication link (the network) so that data from different devices doesn't become jumbled.

Now I would like you to imagine that, instead of just two computers trying to share the printer, there are ten, and they are in a busy sales office. The office might use a dedicated computer (a print server) to handle the data flows between the printer and the users' computers. What happens when the printer or print server breaks down, when the network breaks down or becomes so congested that it can no longer cope with the volume of data being transmitted? Perhaps we need two or more printers, a standby server and an alternative way of routing data to the printers? So there are issues to think about like reliability, cost, capacity and speed.

Maybe you hadn't really thought of the example of computers sending data to printers as a system where devices speak to each other without human intervention. After all, it was a human who initiated the exchange by clicking on the Print icon. It also probably seems quite a long way away from the sort of systems being discussed in the extract you read at

the beginning of this study session. But examining and identifying the building blocks of some simple systems in this way can provide us with tools and a framework to examine more complex systems of the kind hinted at in the article.

In the next few study sessions you'll be looking at some of these building blocks. I shall also identify some of the human issues that can arise. For example, how does a system of devices sending data to each other affect the way we live? It is empowering or disempowering? Does it favour some people above others? Does it threaten or enhance our rights and privacy?

Activity 7 (self-assessment)

Write down two reasons why networked devices need protocols when communicating with each other.

Comment

My answer is given at the end of this part.

Study Session 2: Signals

2.1 Introduction

This study session discusses methods of representing data as it travels from device to device, and some of the processes acting on it during its journey. You will be introduced to a way of expressing large numbers using a method known as scientific notation.

In the final section of this study session you will need to work with a computer.

2.2 Signals

To convey data from one point to another we need to represent the data by means of a signal. We can think of a signal as a deliberate variation in some property of the medium used to convey the data. Some examples are:

- an electrical voltage travelling along copper wires between your telephone and the local exchange;
- pulses of light (though we might not be able to see them) in a fibre-optic cable;
- the radio emissions that are picked up by a mobile telephone or radio receiver.

All these can provide the necessary variations to represent the data. In the first example we can relate the changes in voltage to changes in electrical energy. With the other examples – light and radio waves – we need to think in terms of waves of energy, usually referred to as **electromagnetic radiation**. Electromagnetic radiation is caused by changes in electrical and magnetic fields. Electromagnetic radiation can support signals even when there is no physical medium (such as a cable) involved.

electromagnetic radiation

2.3 Electromagnetic radiation

To help me to explain the nature of the waves of energy known as electromagnetic radiation, I want you to visualise a pond into which a stone has been thrown. If the state of the pond is 'frozen' at an instant in time, the height or depth of the water's surface at that moment will vary with distance from the source of the disturbance. If you were to cut a slice through the pond, you would see a wave shape similar to Figure 3.

The left-hand side is the point where the stone entered the water and the right-hand side is the point where the ripples have died away.

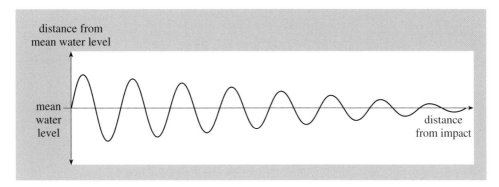

Figure 3 Ripples on a pond

In the pond example, the magnitude of the peaks and troughs of the wave decreases as we move away from the disturbance and the energy is dissipated. We can say that the wave decays. If the energy wasn't dissipated and there was no decay, the shape would be as shown in Figure 4. Waveforms with a periodically repeating curve of this general shape are known as **sinewaves**. You have already met this type of waveform in Part 2, Session 6.

sinewaves

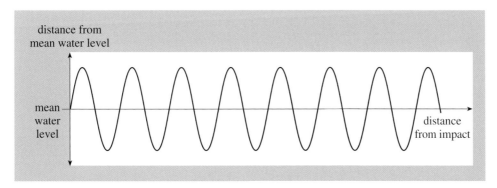

Figure 4 Sinewave

Electromagnetic waves are also sinusoidal (that is, having the shape of a sine wave). If we could freeze an electromagnetic wave at an instant in time, measure its electric or magnetic field strength at different points in space, and plot these measurements on a graph, the shape of the graph would be similar to Figure 4. But it's more usual to measure the strength of its electric or magnetic field at different instants in time as it travels through a single point in space. If we were to do this, measuring the field strength at regular intervals – say every millisecond (one-thousandth of a second) – and plot the results on a graph, it would resemble Figure 5. The wave oscillates regularly and repeatedly with time around its mean value. A single full oscillation is known as a **wave cycle**.

wave cycle

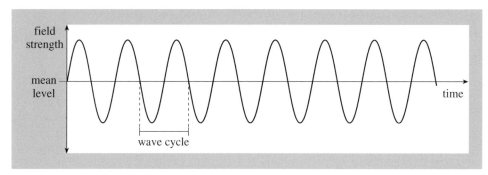

Figure 5 Electromagnetic wave

frequency

Hertz

The **frequency** of the wave is the number of wave cycles it completes in a single second. The unit for measuring frequency is the **Hertz** (Hz). For example, a wave that completes one wave cycle every second has a frequency of 1 Hz; a wave that completes 1000 wave cycles every second has a frequency of 1000 Hz or 1 kHz. Higher frequencies can be expressed in terms of MHz (megahertz – 1 000 000 cycles per second) or GHz (gigahertz – 1 000 000 000 cycles per second.)

electromagnetic spectrum

The term 'electromagnetic spectrum' refers to the entire range of frequencies of electromagnetic waves.

Electromagnetic waves are characterised by their wave frequency. I've already mentioned light waves and radio waves, which are examples of electromagnetic radiation. Other examples are ultraviolet and infrared rays, gamma rays, X-rays and microwaves. These are all names given to groups of electromagnetic waves that behave in a similar manner to each other. Each group occupies a particular space, determined by its range of frequencies, in the **electromagnetic spectrum**. This is shown in Figure 6.

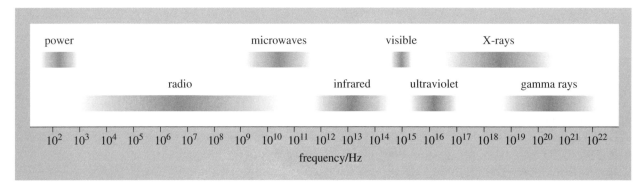

Figure 6 The electromagnetic spectrum

scientific notation

In this figure, the frequency scale is shown in Hertz along the bottom. Notice how the frequencies are expressed – for example, 10^2, 10^3, 10^4, etc. This is a kind of shorthand method – known as **scientific notation** – of expressing large numbers. Scientific notation is explained in the box below. Notice also how the lines representing a particular group of waves are smudged at either end: this is because there are no clear start and end points to the named groups. For example, X-rays are shown to occupy a portion of the electromagnetic spectrum between about

10^{17} Hz and 10^{20} Hz but at the lower end they blur into ultraviolet waves, and at the upper end into gamma rays.

Scientific notation

To express a number in scientific notation the first stage is to divide it successively by 10 until it is reduced to a number that is less than 10. For example, to express the number 4865 in scientific notation I would divide it successively by 10 until I arrived at 4.865. Usually this will result in a number that includes a decimal fraction (the number that follows the decimal point) as well as a whole number part. In my example, 4 is the whole number part and .865 the decimal fraction.

The next stage is to give some indication of how many times the number would have to be multiplied by 10 in order to return it to its original value. In my example I made three successive divisions by 10, so I would have to multiply by 10 three times – that is $10 \times 10 \times 10$ – to return to the original value. So my number could be expressed as $4.865 \times 10 \times 10 \times 10$, but this is hardly a shorthand alternative. So instead of writing $10 \times 10 \times 10$, I can express this as 10^3. The first figure (10 in this case) is known as the **base** and the second figure (3 in this case) is known as the **power** or **exponent** (or sometimes the index). The example would be read as 'ten to the power of three'.

The final stage in scientific notation is to join together the results from the two earlier stages using a multiplication sign giving, in my example, 4.865×10^3.

Any number can be expressed in scientific notation. For example:

$5\,000 = 5 \times 10 \times 10 \times 10 = 5 \times 10^3$

$72\,000 = 7.2 \times 10 \times 10 \times 10 \times 10 = 7.2 \times 10^4$

$82\,600 = 8.26 \times 10 \times 10 \times 10 \times 10 = 8.26 \times 10^4$

Fortunately, there is a quicker way of doing the conversions than by writing out all of the multiplication stages. I'll use the number 7 390 000 to demonstrate the method. Start by imagining there is a decimal point at the right hand end of the number. (I'll add a final 0 so that the decimal point can be seen clearly. This extra 0 is redundant since it doesn't alter the original value at all.)

7 390 000.0

Now move the decimal point one place at a time until it sits after the left-most number, and count the number of places the decimal point has been moved:

7.390 000 0

(decimal point moved 6 places to the left)

Now remove all the 0s at the right-hand end after the decimal point (because these are redundant) and multiply what is left by 10 raised to the power of the number of places the decimal point has been moved.

7.39×10^6

You will often see a number expressed just as the base and the power – for example 10^6 and 10^2. This is interpreted as 1×10^6 ($= 1\,000\,000$) and 1×10^2 ($= 100$).

Activity 8 (self-assessment)

Write the following numbers in scientific notation:

(a) 34 200

(b) 5 340 000 000

(c) 690

(d) 69

Comment

The answers are given at the end of this part.

In the answer to Activity 8, notice how the answer to (d) is expressed in base and power notation as 6.9×10^1 – meaning 'multiply 6.9 by 10 once'. Of course this gives exactly the same result as 6.9×10 and it is just as acceptable to omit the index in cases like these. In fact, it is normal to do so. However I have left it in because I want you to be aware that 10^1 is simply an alternative way of writing 10. Probably you are now wondering why anyone would want to bother with this, since the 'shorthand' ends up longer than the 'longhand' version. For now, just take my word for it that this method of expressing numbers will allow you to perform some arithmetical 'tricks' that can help to simplify some calculations.

In Activity 11, you will learn how to use the Windows calculator to perform calculations on numbers that are expressed in scientific notation. I've placed the activity at the end of the session so that your studies aren't interrupted mid-flow by computer work. However, if you prefer to do this work now, go straight to Section 2.7 and return to this point when you have completed it.

2.4 Modifying the medium to carry the message

Earlier I said that we can think of a signal as a deliberate variation in some property of the medium used to convey the data. Such variation needs to be done in a meaningful way. For example, think of the way pulses of light could be used to convey Morse code. The light could be switched on and off so that a short light pulse could represent a dot and a longer pulse a dash. The same principle can be used with an electrical voltage applied to a copper wire. The sequence of on and off periods could be used to represent data, say, a stream of 1s and 0s. These can be detected and decoded at the receiving end in a communication system.

> Morse code is a code in which letters and numbers are represented by groups of short dots and long dashes.

In radio signals, some property of the electromagnetic wave could be varied in a meaningful way – its frequency, for example. This is shown in Figure 7. Here I have indicated a number of equal time intervals. In the first interval, the wave completes three whole cycles, but during the second, third and fourth intervals, the wave completes only one and a half cycles per interval. So in these intervals the frequency of the wave is half the frequency of the first interval. Similarly, during periods 5, 6 and 8 the wave completes three whole cycles per interval, and only half that in intervals 7, 9 and 10. These changes of frequency can be detected and interpreted as data – say a 1 or a 0 depending on the frequency of wave during the measured interval.

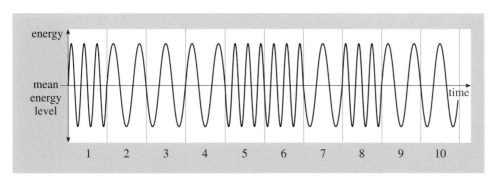

Figure 7 Representing data with frequency changes

The electromagnetic wave can be described as a **carrier** because it carries the data. That is, some property has been modified to represent the data. The process of modifying the carrier in this way is called **modulation**. A **transmitter** takes the data from the sender, modifies the carrier, and then sends the resulting signal through the communication link. At the receiving end, a **receiver** takes the signal, and extracts the data by a process known as **demodulation**, then passes the data to the recipient. The process is shown in Figure 8.

> carrier
>
> modulation
>
> transmitter
>
> receiver
>
> demodulation

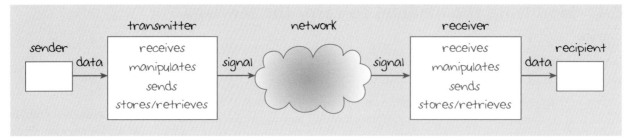

Figure 8 A transmitter and receiver in a network

Figure 8 is in many ways similar to the diagrams I used earlier in Figures 1 and 2 but it is slightly more abstract in some parts. For example, users are no longer shown, nor are named computing devices like a printer or computer. Instead I am showing the end points as rectangles labelled 'sender' and 'recipient'. These rectangles could be computers or printers, but could also be other devices. There may well be human users on the other side of them, but I am not concerned with those in this model so I have omitted them.

Another abstraction is the cloud that represents the network. This also has been done to simplify the diagram. I've chosen to focus on the parts that are most relevant to my discussion (which concerns the transmitter and receiver) and for this purpose I'm not concerned with what is happening in the network links. The cloud indicates that there is something going on there but doesn't give any detail of what it is.

Notice in Figure 8 how I've shown the communication to be flowing in one direction only. This is because the transmitter receives data only from the sender and sends it only to the receiver. In this model there is no communication in the opposite direction. Some devices, known as **transceivers,** perform both the sending and receiving of signals so they could replace both the transmitter and receiver shown in the figure.

transceiver

Activity 9 (exploratory)

How would you modify Figure 8 to model the use of transceivers in place of both the transmitter and receiver?

Comment

The modifications needed would be:
- the end points both become sender/recipient because both can send or receive;
- the transmitter and receiver are both replaced by transceivers;
- the arrows showing the communication flow now run in both directions.

These modifications are shown in Figure 9.

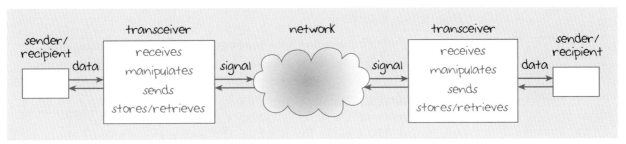

Figure 9 Transceivers in a network

2.5 Propagation delay

The time taken for a signal to travel from its source to its destination is known as **propagation delay**. This is derived from the verb 'propagate' which in a physics context means 'spread' or 'travel'. The propagation delay depends on a number of factors, including the distance the signal has to travel and the signal's speed.

propagation delay

Contemporary physics states that nothing can travel faster than the speed of light (or any electromagnetic wave) in a vacuum which, to the nearest metre, is 299 792 458 metres per second. This is a rather precise measurement and for most purposes we don't need to work to this degree of accuracy. You are more likely to see the speed of light given as 'approximately 3×10^8 m/s' (that is 300 000 000 metres per second).

> *It is often acceptable to round numbers up or down to make calculations simpler. The result won't be completely precise, but it will probably be close enough for many purposes You've already met this idea earlier in the course. The box below takes the idea a little further and explains the principles.*

It's important to realise that not all carriers are able to achieve the speed of light. A voltage pulse travelling in a copper cable has a speed of approximately 2×10^8 m/s. Signals can also be delayed by the processes required to manipulate and manage them on their journey from sender to receiver.

Rounding numbers

The more digits there are in a number, the less contribution the digits at the right-hand end make to the magnitude of the number. Consider Table 1. Incrementing 9 by 1 results in an increase of the original number by almost one-tenth. Incrementing 99 by 1 results in an increase of the original number by almost one-hundredth, and so on. The longer the number, the less is the effect of an increase in the right-most digit. Or, put another way, the longer the number, the less significant the right-most digit becomes.

Table 1   Fractional comparisons

Original number	New number	Fractional increase	Approximate fraction of original number
9	10	1/9	one-tenth
99	100	1/99	one-hundredth
999	1 000	1/999	one-thousandth
9 999	10 000	1/9 999	one ten-thousandth
99 999	100 000	1/99 999	one hundred-thousandth
999 999	1 000 000	1/999 999	one-millionth

This means that in long numbers we can often disregard some of the digits at the right-hand end because they are not significant. Disregarding them will introduce very little error because they make very little contribution to the overall value. It is the digits at the left-hand end that are significant, and we can select the degree of accuracy required by choosing how many left-hand digits we consider to be significant for our purposes. We call these significant figures. Then we round the original number up or down until all but the required significant figures are shown as 0s.

For example, take the number 3482. Let's say I decide that I need to work with 3 significant figures. In this case I would round the original number down to 3480 because 3482 is closer to 3480 than it is to 3490.

Let's say instead that I decide to work with 2 significant figures. In this case I would round 3482 up to 3500 because 3482 is closer to 3500 than it is to 3400.

When we round a number up or down in this way it is important to indicate what we have done by stating that the rounded number is approximate, or by stating how many significant figures we are working to. Thus 3482 becomes:

3480 (correct to 3 significant figures)

or

3500 (correct to 2 significant figures)

These rules apply just the same when we are working with long numbers that include a decimal point, or with long numbers expressed in scientific notation. For example 2.14565879×10^8 would become 2.146×10^8 (correct to 4 significant figures), or 2.15×10^8 (correct to 3 significant figures).

The speed of light in a vacuum (299 792 458 m/s) gives a good example of why it can sometimes be useful to express how many significant figures we are working to. The figure becomes:

299 800 000 (correct to 4 significant figures)

and

300 000 000 (correct to 3 significant figures)

because the rounding (up in this case) gives a result that might otherwise be taken to be correct to only 1 significant figure.

2.6 Attenuation and distortion

As a signal travels from one device to another it has two problems to overcome. The first is that it gets weaker the further it travels, because some of its energy is absorbed by the transmission medium. This effect is known as **attenuation**. The extent of attenuation depends on the distance it has to travel and on the type of medium it is travelling through. An amplifier can be used to boost the signal power at the transmitter and receiver, and if necessary at various points in the transmission link, so that signal power can be maintained at a usable level.

attenuation

The second problem is that the signal can become distorted by external influences as it travels along the communication path. This can be caused by other signals travelling in the vicinity, or by waves of energy such as solar energy, lightning, and pulses of energy from electrical machinery. You might have come across instances of distortion in your own domestic equipment. For example, I have a small TV in my bedroom and when I use my hairdryer nearby I can see spots and lines on the TV screen that are caused by the electromagnetic energy generated by the motor in the hairdryer. If I place my mobile phone next to my radio I often hear 'beeps' on my radio as the phone sends signals to the phone network.

Unless distortion can be removed from the signal at the receiving end then any amplification to overcome the problems of attenuation will also amplify any distortion in the received signal. Binary signals are quite resistant to distortion because they represent only two states that can usually be distinguished quite easily from any unwanted effects.

Activity 10 (self-assessment)

To test your understanding of what you have read so far about signals, try to write down answers to these questions.

1   The frequency of an electromagnetic wave is measured in units of _____

2   In what portion of the electromagnetic spectrum does an electromagnetic wave with a frequency of 10^8 Hz lie?

3   What is meant by the term 'modulation'?

4   Why might a signal become attenuated as it travels?

Comment

The answers are at the end of this part.

2.7   Working with scientific notation using the Windows calculator

For this final section you will need to work with your computer.

Most electronic calculators will enable you to perform calculations on numbers expressed in scientific notation. This section will take you through an exercise using the Windows calculator to perform the following calculation:

$$(3 \times 10^4) \times (2 \times 10^3)$$

Notice how I have placed the two terms in brackets. Often this is done to ensure that each step of a calculation is done in the right order. Here it isn't strictly necessary to include brackets since, when multiplying together a number of terms, the result is the same regardless of order. However, brackets do help to tidy things up and show which terms belong together.

> **The > symbol represents the small black triangle shown on the right of a menu item, which indicates a sub-menu.**

Start the Windows calculator running on your computer (go to the Start menu and select Programs > Accessories > Calculator) then follow each step shown in the table below.

Step	Action	Calculator display
1	Make sure the Windows calculator is in Scientific mode by selecting Scientific from the View menu.	0.
2	Enter 3	3.
3	Click the Exp button which you will find in the left half of the calculator keyboard. ('Exp' stands for 'exponent') This tells the calculator that the next number you enter will be a power of 10 and that you are working in scientific notation. The 'e' now showing on the display indicates that the number you have entered is displayed in scientific notation.	3.e + 0
4	Enter 4. The display is now showing the equivalent of 3×10^4. You have now finished entering the term in the first set of brackets.	3.e + 4
5	Click the multiply (*) button. This tells the calculator that you want to multiply the number showing in the display by some other number. The display now changes to show the number you have entered in its full form ($3 \times 10^4 = 30000$).	30000.
6	You will now start to enter the term in the second set of brackets. Enter 2	2.
7	Click the Exp button	2.e + 0
8	Enter 3. The display is now showing the equivalent of 2×10^3. You have now finished entering the term in the second set of brackets.	2.e + 3
9	Click the equal (=) button. This tells the calculator that you want it to display the result of the calculation. This is shown in its full form.	60000000.
10	Finally, you can force the calculator to display the result of the calculation in scientific notation. Do this by clicking the F-E button which you will find in the left half of the calculator keyboard. ('F-E' stands for 'fixed to exponent') The display is now showing the result in the 'shorthand' form which you can interpret as 6×10^7.	6.e + 7

The result of the above exercise shows that $(3 \times 10^4) \times (2 \times 10^3) = 6 \times 10^7$. Simple calculations like these can, in fact, be carried out quite easily without the need for a calculator, as I will explain below.

In calculations where terms are multiplied, the order of the terms isn't important and will not affect the result, so:

$$(3 \times 10^4) \times (2 \times 10^3) = 3 \times 2 \times 10^4 \times 10^3$$

Writing this in full would give:

$$3 \times 2 \times (10 \times 10 \times 10 \times 10) \times (10 \times 10 \times 10).$$

Since:

$$10 \times 10 \times 10 \times 10 \times 10 \times 10 \times 10 = 10^7$$

I hope you can see that:

$$10^4 \times 10^3 = 10^{(4+3)} = 10^7$$

and therefore:

$$(3 \times 10^4) \times (2 \times 10^3) = 3 \times 2 \times 10^{(4+3)} = 6 \times 10^7$$

So when multiplying together two or more terms expressed in scientific notation, a shortcut to the result is to add the powers.

Sometimes the calculation will require a little more manipulation in order to express the result in scientific notation. For example:

$$(8 \times 10^6) \times (3.5 \times 10^3)$$
$$= 8 \times 3.5 \times 10^{(6+3)}$$
$$= 28 \times 10^9$$
$$= 2.8 \times 10^1 \times 10^9$$
$$= 2.8 \times 10^{10}$$

Similar principles can be used when dividing terms expressed in scientific notation. A shortcut to the result is to subtract the powers.

To demonstrate I'll evaluate (3×10^4) divided by (2×10^3):

$$\frac{3 \times 10^4}{2 \times 10^3} = \frac{3 \times 10 \times 10 \times 10 \times 10}{2 \times 10 \times 10 \times 10} = \frac{3 \times 10}{2} = 1.5 \times 10^1$$

I hope you can see from this that:

$$\frac{3 \times 10^4}{2 \times 10^3} = \frac{3}{2} \times 10^{(4-3)} = 1.5 \times 10^1$$

Activity 11 (self-assessment)

(a) Use the 'short-cut' method to evaluate the following, write down your answers and then check your results using the Windows calculator:

   (i) $(5 \times 10^2) \times (7 \times 10^3)$

   (ii) $\dfrac{4 \times 10^5}{2 \times 10^2}$

(b) Use the Windows calculator to evaluate the following, write down your answers correct to three significant figures:

(i) $(8.55 \times 10^4) \times (5.04 \times 10^6)$

(ii) $(5.24 \times 10^2) \times (7.53 \times 10^3)$

Comment

The answers are given at the end of this part.

If any of your answers differ from mine, it is probably because you entered an incorrect value or clicked on the wrong key. If this happens, try the calculation again.

Study Session 3: Wired networks

3.1   Introduction

This study session starts by broadly classifying different types of network, first by the nature of the communication links used to connect devices and then by a network's geographical spread. It then examines in more detail a network which uses a cabled communication link.

node

A networked device is often referred to as a node so I shall use this term in the sections that follow. A **node** is any device (for example, computer, printer, server) connected to a network, either as an end point (that is, a point where the communication link terminates) or some intermediary point (that is, a point which lies between end points on a communication link). To send data from one node to another there must be some kind of communication path between them. One option is for nodes to be physically linked to each other by a cable – for example, copper or fibre-optic cable. Each node must have a physical connection to the cable in order to send and receive data. Networks that use a physical communication link such as these are known as 'wired networks'. Wireless networks (which I shall discuss in the next study session) have no physical connections between the nodes.

Local Area Networks

Personal Area Networks

Networks can also be broadly classified according to their geographical spread: **Local Area Networks** (LANs) connect together a number of nodes within a single building or group of buildings situated close to each other. A LAN can connect together as few as two or three nodes or hundreds of nodes. You will also come across references to **Personal Area Networks** (PANs) which cover small areas such as a home, a single room within a home or even a car. A PAN is a type of LAN.

Wide Area Networks

Wide Area Networks (WANs) connect together two or more LANs that are geographically separated. This is done by using links between LANs. A WAN could connect together all the LANs in offices of a national company and could even cross international boundaries.

This study session will focus only on LANs. It will introduce you to the basic principles of operation of wired LANs, and in particular to a network technology known as Ethernet. Ethernet is the dominant technology used in LANs.

3.2   Wired networks – principles of operation

network interface card

Each node in a network needs processes to control the flow of data over the network. These processes are carried out by a **network interface card** (NIC), which provides the interface between the node and the communication link. The NIC enables the physical connection to be made to the network.

Each node also needs a way of distinguishing it from all the other nodes on the network. This can be thought of as an address that other nodes use when they want to send data to a particular destination. Each node is assigned an identity number known as its **Media Access Control (MAC) address.**

Messages between nodes aren't sent in one continuous stream but are broken up into small chunks called **frames** which are sent one at a time. You can think of a frame as being a particular type of the packets that you met in Part 1. Each frame includes some information which enables it to be routed through the network and delivered to the intended destination. All frames include the MAC address of both the destination node and the sending node. In some networks, frames are not routed specifically to the destination node but are sent to every node on the network. Each node reads the destination address and picks out those frames where the destination address matches its own.

As you learned in Study Session 2, the signals representing data get weaker the further they travel. This is one of the factors that could limit the maximum length of a communication link in a LAN. This limitation is overcome by the use of repeaters. A **repeater** increases the practical distance between nodes by regenerating the signal and passing it on.

3.3 Wired network configurations

Network nodes can be connected together in different arrangements known as topologies. I shall describe four common topologies that you may come across.

The simplest type is known as a **bus** topology. This is one where all the nodes connect to a single network cable and can communicate with every other attached node by placing a message onto the cable. A simplified representation of the layout of a bus topology is shown in Figure 10(a). To understand the diagram, imagine you are floating above the network and looking down. The circles represent the network nodes and the lines connecting them represent the communication links.

In a bus topology, each node connects to the same cable, so a frame sent by one node will arrive at every other node. Each node must read the destination MAC address in the frame to decide whether or not to accept it. If any node becomes inoperable, all the other nodes are still able to communicate with each other, but any cable failure will result in the loss of communication between nodes on opposite sides of the failure point.

In a **star** topology (Figure 10(b)) each node has its own cabled link to a central point called a **hub**. All messages are conveyed through the hub and, like the bus topology, will arrive at each node. In this arrangement,

Media Access Control (MAC) address

frame

repeater

bus

star

hub

any single cable failure affects only one node, but a hub failure would make the entire network inoperable. Typically, the maximum number of nodes that can be connected together in a star topology is 24.

To expand a star network, hubs may be joined together so that nodes connected to one hub can communicate with nodes connected to another hub. This results in an **extended star** topology (Figure 10(c)).

extended star

Depending on the mode of operation, in some bus, star and extended star topologies, only one node at a time is allowed to place a frame onto the network. This means that every node has to compete with every other node for access to the network. As a network grows and traffic increases, a point is reached where competition becomes so great that the network becomes unacceptably slow.

segments

switch

bridge

A way of expanding the network to overcome the problems of competition is to stop sending all frames to every node and instead to separate the network into **segments**. A segment is a discrete portion of a network in which all nodes share the communication link. Segments are then joined together with a device known as a **switch** or **bridge** (Figure 10(d)). Such a device will examine each frame as it arrives and read the destination MAC address to establish whether or not to pass the frame onto an adjacent segment. A segment will receive only frames destined for nodes within it or frames that need to be routed through it to reach other segments further along the network. In some networks each segment could contain just a single node.

mesh

A **mesh** network has a web-like structure. In a full mesh topology (Figure 10(e)) each node has a point-to-point link with every other node. In a partial mesh topology (Figure 10(f)) some nodes have connections to a number of other nodes, but some may be connected to only one other node. Data between two nodes may have to travel through intermediary nodes before reaching its destination. In a partial mesh topology the nodes must have some knowledge of the network layout so that messages can be routed correctly. If a node or a communication link fails it is often possible to find another path to the destination, so mesh-type networks have high reliability.

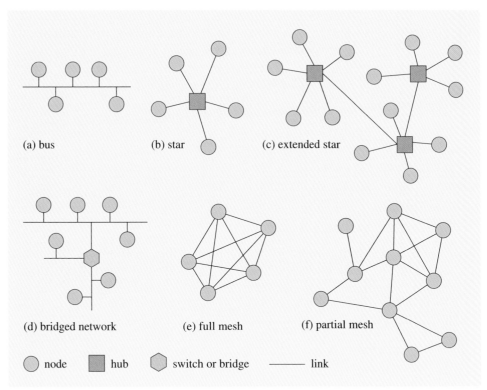

Figure 10 Representations of network topologies

Activity 12 (self-assessment)

To test your understanding of what you have read so far about wired networks, try to write down a short answer (a sentence or two) to these questions.

1   What is the term often used to describe devices connected to a wired network?
2   What is the purpose of the MAC address?
3   How does a repeater address the problem of attenuation?
4   How does a switch or a bridge make it possible to expand a network?

Comment

The answers are given at the end of this part.

3.4   Protocols and standards

In earlier parts of this block you have already met the idea of protocols – rules to govern how information is sent, transmitted and received. Protocols can be explained using an analogy with the way people talk to each other. When we talk we don't simply string words together in

a random fashion: we have a set of rules (grammar) that determines the order of words and the way sentences are constructed. *Understand didn't have other us difficult if it would be quite rules each these for to we.* I hope the previous string of words illustrates what I mean! It's a jumbled-up version of the sentence 'If we didn't have these rules it would be quite difficult for us to understand each other.'

We also need to have a shared understanding of what a word means (for example, the word 'trunk' may have quite different meanings in North America and Britain). But we have thousands of versions of these rules – different languages and dialects – so simply having a set of rules isn't enough to ensure good communication. We have to agree to use the *same* rules (or at least nearly the same rules) or have some mechanism to translate from one set of rules to another.

standard

Fortunately a number of organisations have taken responsibility for ensuring that particular communication protocols are clearly stated, recorded and made available to others. These organisations agree on and produce the necessary **standards**, which you may remember are a kind of technical specification that sets out the rules and requirements to ensure interoperability. A standards document is drawn up with the involvement and agreement of all interested parties, for example representatives of users, manufacturers and government agencies. The dominant standard in wired LANs is one that is commonly known as

Ethernet

Ethernet.

3.5   Establishing Ethernet standards

The first Ethernet network was developed in the early 1970s, long before the days of the World Wide Web and personal computers (PCs). It was designed by researchers at the Xerox Palo Alto Research Centre in California, USA to connect the Centre's 'Alto' computers to an office printer.

open standards

Ethernet's journey from its modest roots to become the dominant network technology is a fascinating one. One of the main reasons for its success lies with the decision to publish the standard. Standards that are available to anyone in this way are known as **open standards**.

Activity 13 (exploratory)

Try to think of a standardised product that you use in your own home. Make some notes about what features of the product are standardised. Why do you think that the availability of Open Standards helps to establish related products in the marketplace?

Comment

One simple example of a standardised product that I thought of is the plug that connects my domestic electrical equipment (such as my kettle, hairdryer, table lamps) to the mains electricity supply. In the UK, these plugs have three pins and conform to a standard known as BS1363. BS stands for 'British Standard' and indicates that the standard has been agreed by the British Standards Institute – the national standards body of the UK. BS1363 specifies things like the shape and configuration of the pins, the type of material various parts of the plug should be manufactured from, and the safety features it should possess. Other countries use different standards for their electrical plugs and sockets so when I travel abroad I generally need an adaptor to use the electrical equipment I take with me.

When a standard is widely available, many different manufacturers are able to produce products that are compatible. This is likely to increase competition and drive down the costs to consumers. It is also likely to increase manufacturers' confidence in the market and so encourages them to invest in and develop products. This in turn is likely to lead to greater reliability.

The standardising body for Ethernet is the IEEE. (You may remember that the article *Networked microsensors and the end of the world as we know it* that you met in Study Session 1 was published by the IEEE.)

The Institute of Electrical and Electronics Engineers (IEEE)

The IEEE was formed from two earlier organisations: the American Institute of Electrical Engineers (AIEE) and the Institute of Radio Engineers (IRE). As technology developed, the boundaries between these two organisations became more and more blurred and eventually, in 1963, they merged. The IEEE is based in the USA but is essentially a global association of professionals working in technical areas such as computing, telecommunications, power engineering and electronics.

When developing standards, it is usual for the IEEE to establish a committee of interested bodies. This committee forms a working group to collaborate and agree on the details of the proposed standard. The working group set up to standardise network technologies took its name from the month and year (February 1980) of its formation, and became known as the '802 working group'. Task forces appointed to work on particular aspects of networking are each identified by a further number. The Ethernet taskforce and Ethernet standards are all identified by IEEE 802.3.

The IEEE 802.3 standard specifies a total data rate of 10 Mbps, but subsequent developments in technology enable faster data rates to be achieved and so new 802.3 standards have been defined, providing data

rates of 100 Mbps, 1 Gbps (gigabits per second) or 10 Gbps. These new standards are identified by adding a suffix to the standard number so, for example, the 10 Gbps Ethernet standard is known as IEEE 802.3ae.

I find it's quite difficult to get a feel for the magnitude of data rates like those I quoted in the previous paragraph. When I meet a very large number, I find it is helpful to compare it with something relevant that I do have a 'feel' for (for example, something I'm familiar with in everyday life). It doesn't have to be an exact comparison – just an estimate helps. The next activity will give you an example of a simple comparison you could make.

Activity 14 (exploratory)

Estimate how many times faster the data rate of the original Ethernet standard (10 Mbps) is, compared to the data rate of a modern standard dial-up modem of 56 kbps. (Hint: round down the dial-up modem rate to 50 kbps.)

Comment

I suggested you round down the dial-up modem rate to 50 kbps becomes it then becomes a much easier figure to work with, so this speeds up the calculations. Because only an estimate is required, you don't need to come up with an exact answer, just one that will help you to make a rough comparison.

First I need to express both figures in the same units. Currently one is expressed as Mbps and the other as kbps, so I will express them both in bps.

10 Mbps = 10 000 000 bps

50 kbps = 50 000 bps

$$\frac{10\ 000\ 000}{50\ 000} = 200$$

So the first commercial Ethernet network was about 200 times faster than a modern 56 kbps modem dial-up connection.

Comparisons and estimates are two very useful tools. A comparison with something you are already familiar with can help you to get a feel for new ideas or concepts. (For example, I can get a feel for the size of a hectare once I know it is about the same size as a soccer pitch of international standard.) As well as providing a quick way of making comparisons, estimates can also be useful in checking that the answers you come up with for calculations are sensible.

3.6 Routers

One type of network device I haven't mentioned is a **router**. This is because a router generally works at the edge of a LAN rather than within it. A router can operate at a level that is independent of specific LAN protocols so it can be used to join an Ethernet LAN with a LAN that uses different protocols. A router holds information about the structure of a network and can make decisions about how data should be routed through it. As well as being used to connect together different types of LAN, a router connects different types of network. For example a router would be used to connect a LAN to a WAN.

router

Study Session 4: Wireless networks

4.1 Introduction

The focus of Study Session 3 was on LANs that use some kind of physical medium (for example, copper wires or fibre-optic cables) to connect together network nodes. In this session I'll be examining wireless networks – that is, networks that transmit data through the air (or space) using radio waves.

There's nothing new about wireless: the principles of transmitting information using radio waves were discovered over a century ago. However, using radio waves to provide the transmission links in a network is a relatively new and fast-growing technology. It enables us to connect into networks in public places like airports and city centres without needing a wired link.

You may already know a little about using radio waves to connect into a network. You may have heard or read news reports that discuss wireless networks. You may even have some experience of using them yourself. If you use a mobile phone, Bluetooth®-enabled device, or connect your computer to a network using WiFi then your communications will be using radio waves.

In this and the next study session I shall be outlining some of the principles of wireless transmission and then looking in more detail at two particular wireless standards – WiFi and Bluetooth. I'll also be discussing some of the issues arising from the deployment of wireless networks.

Activity 15 (exploratory)

(a) Spend a short time – not more than 3 or 4 minutes – jotting down some notes on what you know about how wireless networks operate. (If you don't know anything about wireless networks yet, just move on to the next part of the activity.)

(b) Based on what you have learned about wired LANs in Study Session 3, jot down a few things you would like to know about wireless networks.

Comment

Of course, I can't guess what you already know or would like to know. Your notes might be about what equipment is needed, what data rates are possible, whether there is a limit on the distance between nodes or a limit on the number of nodes a wireless network can support. Or they might be something different.

The value in this activity is that you have thought about two important questions: 'What do I already know about this topic?' and 'What further things would I like to know about this topic?' Many people find that this sort of approach helps them to become more active in their learning because it gives them a focus and helps them to engage more effectively with the topic. See if it works for you.

4.2 Basic principles of wireless transmission

I've never quite lost the sense of wonder at the way information can be transmitted with no visible link between the sender and recipient. When I was a child I used to think that sound came through the wire linking my family's radio to the mains electricity supply (I was born before the days of battery-powered transistor radios) and I couldn't understand why my parents referred to it as 'the wireless' – since clearly it wasn't. I now know that the wire simply fed the radio with the electrical power it needed. The radio signals were picked up by a special electrical conductor called an **antenna**. (Another name for antenna is **aerial** and you are likely to see these terms used interchangeably, both within this course and elsewhere.)

antenna

aerial

Radio signals arrive through the air as fluctuations in the electromagnetic field of a radio wave. This induces a fluctuating electrical current to flow in the antenna. These fluctuations are detected and translated into data. But an antenna can be used in two different ways. Fluctuations in electrical current flowing in an antenna can also emit a radio signal, so an antenna can be used to both receive and send radio signals. Most devices operating in radio networks are transceivers (that is, they can both send and receive radio signals) and will use the same antenna when sending and receiving. Figure 8 (Study Session 2), can be developed to represent a wireless network. This is shown in Figure 11 where I have broken down the components within the radio transceiver to show the antenna and the signal processing components.

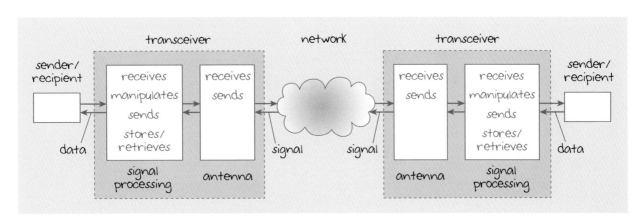

Figure 11 Representation of a wireless network

wavefront

The term 'wavefront' refers to all points on a wave that are equidistant from its source.

When signals are travelling in cables, they follow the path of the cable, even though this may twist and turn. For this reason, cables are described as 'guided' media. Radio signals are not guided in this way. The electromagnetic waves carrying the signal can propagate in all directions, and may spread out in a spherical pattern as shown in Figure 12. The wavefronts are represented by the concentric circles in both figures. Notice how the circles become fainter with distance from the centre, representing the way the signal weakens. Figure 12(a) shows a representation of a side view of an antenna. In practice antennas come in many shapes and sizes, but this representation is often used in diagrams regardless of the actual design of the antenna. In Figure 12(b) I have shown a representation looking down onto the antenna.

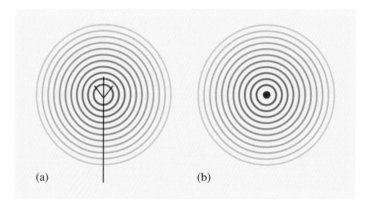

Figure 12   Electromagnetic energy radiating from a non-directional antenna: (a) side view; (b) from above

Antennas can be designed to be directional so that the signal power is directed into a beam (Figure 13). This allows the signal to travel further for the same power. However, in general, the attenuation of a radio signal is greater than the attenuation of a signal travelling an equivalent distance via a cable.

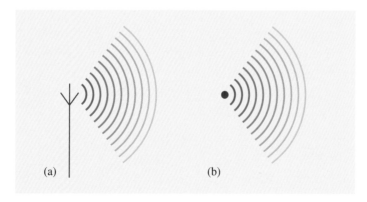

Figure 13   Electromagnetic energy radiating from a directional antenna: (a) side view; (b) from above

The maximum practical distance that a signal can be propagated is influenced by factors such as the signal frequency and strength, the physical environment and the design of the antenna. Low-frequency waves can travel further than high-frequency waves. Low-frequency waves are also more efficient at penetrating physical barriers such as walls and floors – something that high-frequency waves, like visible light, can't do. So it is the waves at the lower frequency end of the electromagnetic spectrum that are used for over-the-air communications. These include the radio and microwave frequencies.

Activity 16 (self-assessment)

Refer back to Figure 6 in Study Session 2. Approximately what section of the electromagnetic spectrum is occupied by radio waves? (That is, at approximately what frequency do they start and at approximately what frequency do they finish?)

Comment

The answer is given at the end of this part.

From the answer to Activity 16, we can calculate the approximate frequency range of radio waves. This is the difference between the highest and lowest frequencies in that section which, in this case, is somewhere around 10^{10} Hz minus 10^3 Hz (10 000 000 000 Hz minus 1 000 Hz). If I were to calculate an answer from these figures the result would be 9 999 999 000 Hz or approximately 10^{10} Hz.

You may have been surprised to find that the result of deducting 1 000 Hz (1 kHz) from 10 000 000 000 Hz (10 GHz) gave an approximate result of 10 000 000 000 (10 GHz). After all, we have taken something away from the original 10 GHz so how can the answer be approximately the same as the figure we started with? This is because 10 GHz is extremely large compared to 1 kHz – in fact 10 million (10^7) times greater. So subtracting 1 kHz is insignificant.

4.3   Regulation

Increasing demand for wireless technology means that the radio frequencies must be carefully managed and allocated by governments to satisfy all the different users and to prevent interference between them. (You may remember the UK Government's auction of 3G radio licences in Spring 2000 which raised approximately £22.5 billion.)

Before transmitting radio signals, organisations must usually obtain a licence permitting them to use a specified frequency or band of frequencies. However, one band of radio frequencies is available internationally for unlicensed users. These are the frequencies lying between 2.4000 GHz and 2.4835 GHz. These frequencies – usually referred to simply as the 2.4 GHz frequency band – are collectively known as the industrial, scientific and medical (ISM) radio band. (Some countries also allocate additional frequencies for unlicensed users.)

In the remainder of this study session I shall introduce two wireless standards that are designed to operate within the ISM band of radio frequencies. These are WiFi, developed by the IEEE and covered by the IEEE 802.11 family of wireless LAN standards, and Bluetooth, developed by the Bluetooth Special Interest Group (SIG) and covered by the IEEE 802.15 family of wireless PAN standards.

4.4   WiFi

WiFi (from 'Wireless Fidelity') is used to connect devices together in one of two network configurations known as 'ad hoc' and 'infrastructure'. I shall explain these terms shortly. (As a starting point, though, you could look up the terms 'ad hoc' and 'infrastructure' in your dictionary.)

stations

In wireless LANs, nodes are usually referred to as **stations** – probably because each communicating device acts as a radio station with transmitter and receiver. These functions, and the necessary control functions, are provided by a wireless network interface card (wireless NIC) in a similar way to wired networks.

4.4.1   Network Structure
A WiFi network can operate in one of two different modes.

Ad hoc mode
In an ad hoc network, stations communicate with each other directly, without the need for any intermediary or central control. This means that when one WiFi device comes within range of another, a direct communication channel can be set up between them. This is known as **peer-to-peer communication**. Additional devices can join the network, all communicating with each other in a broadcast fashion. (In this context, 'broadcast' means that a message sent by one node will arrive at every other node in the network, regardless of the destination address.)

peer-to-peer communication

Figure 14 provides a diagram of a possible geographical layout of an ad hoc network. This figure is similar to the diagrams of network topologies you met in Study Session 3, in that it is a representation of a network layout viewed as though you were floating above it and looking down. In Figure 14, the dark circles represent WiFi stations. The concentric

circles around them show that the communication channel is radio waves. In this case, my diagram indicates non-directional antennas. However, since the focus of this diagram is the network layout, then the detail of whether directional or non-directional antennas are used isn't important.

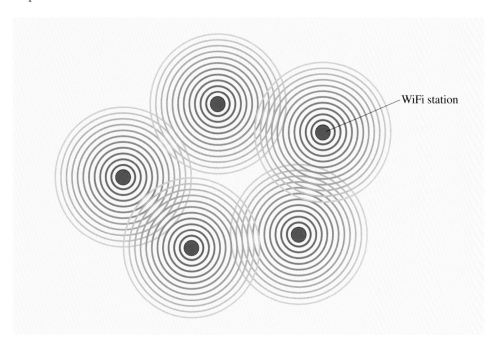

WiFi station

Figure 14   Representation of a WiFi ad hoc network

An ad hoc network is likely to be temporary – for example, a network set up for a business meeting where people want to share information stored on portable devices like lap-top computers and personal digital assistants (PDAs). (If you looked up the term 'ad hoc' in your dictionary you probably found a definition something like 'for a specific purpose, impromptu, not pre-planned'.) An ad hoc network is independent of, and isolated from, any other network.

Infrastructure mode

In infrastructure mode (Figure 15), stations communicate with each other via a wireless **access point** (AP) which also acts as a connector between a wired network and the wireless network. The access point is effectively a base station that controls the communication between the other stations. Access points form part of a wired network infrastructure and are not mobile. (If you looked up the word 'infrastructure' in your dictionary the definition given probably used terms like 'underlying foundation, basic structure, substructure'.)

access point

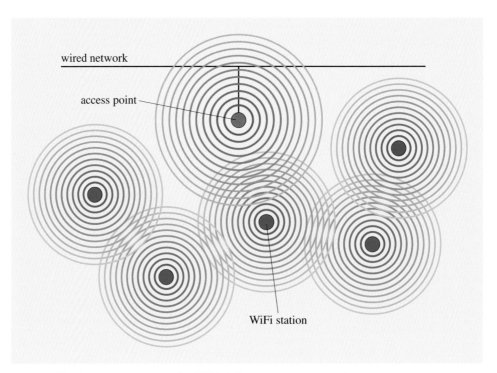

Figure 15   Representation of a WiFi infrastructure network

4.4.2   How WiFi stations find each other

A WiFi station determines whether it is in range of an AP by transmitting an enquiry, known as a probe request frame, and waiting for a response. If more than one AP responds, the station will choose to communicate with the one that has the strongest signal. A probe request frame initiates the WiFi connection and is an example of a management frame – a type of frame that does not carry any message data.

Just like the nodes on an Ethernet network, each station must have a means of being uniquely identified by a MAC address. Every message data frame sent must contain the MAC address of the source, destination and access point, as well as other management data that enables the frames to be correctly sequenced and errors to be detected.

4.4.3   Sharing the medium

Because all the stations in a WiFi network share the same communication channel, only one station at a time can be allowed to send data. So a station waits until it detects a period of inactivity and then uses a special protocol which prevents two or more stations sending data at exactly the same time. The exchanges involved in these protocols are another example of management data.

4.4.4 Data rate

Just as for Ethernet, developments in technology have increased the achievable data rates since the first WiFi standard was developed in 1997. At the time of writing, the latest WiFi standard to be published – IEEE 802.11g – defines a data rate of 54 Mbps.

Activity 17 (exploratory)

How do you think the rate for transmitting messages between stations is affected by:

- the management information that is included with each frame;
- the protocols used to enable multiple stations to share the communication channel;
- multiple users on a WiFi network?

Comment

Both the management information and the sharing protocols impose an overhead that uses up some of the capacity of the communication channel. This effectively reduces the capacity available for sending message data (as compared to management data). The effective data rate will, therefore, be lower than the value quoted.

When thinking about the effects of multiple users on the network, it's also important to realise that the data rate quoted is the maximum that can be achieved, and this has to be shared out between all the users of the network. As the number of users increases, the data rate available to each individual user decreases.

The practical message data rate that can be achieved in a wireless network is often described as its **throughput**. Even in ideal operating conditions, the throughput may be only 50% to 75% of the maximum data rate. For WiFi, throughput is generally about half the maximum data rate possible on the communication channel, giving about 30 Mbps for 802.11g networks, and this has to be shared between all the stations on the network.

throughput

4.4.5 Operating range

The achievable data rate reduces with distance from the AP (or in the case of an ad hoc network, with distance from other stations). Maximum data rates can be achieved only within about 30 m of an AP, tailing off at distances greater than this. For 802.11g networks the data rate drops to as low as 1 or 2 Mbps at 100 m. Physical barriers such as partitions and walls will further reduce the maximum rate possible at a given distance from the AP.

4.4.6   Number of stations

The WiFi standards do not define any upper limit on the number of stations that can join a network, though some particular equipment manufacturers may specify a limit. (I've seen one which stipulates a maximum of 128 stations connected to any one AP.) However, you should appreciate from my earlier discussion that, as the number of communicating stations increases, the channel capacity available for each station decreases. A point will eventually be reached when the network becomes too congested to provide an adequate service.

Activity 18 (self-assessment)

To test your understanding of what you have read so far about WiFi, say whether each of the statements below is true or false.

(a) In ad hoc mode, WiFi stations are connected to a wired network via an access point.

(b) All stations connected to a WiFi network in infrastructure mode will be able to achieve identical data rates.

(c) Every WiFi station requires a MAC address.

(d) Throughput is a term that describes the maximum data rate of a WiFi network.

Comment

The answers are given at the end of this part.

4.5   Bluetooth

The driving force for the development of the Bluetooth standard was to eliminate the need for connecting wires between local ICT devices such as keyboards, monitors, printers, PDAs (Personal Digital Assistants), cell phones and headsets. This was already possible using infrared technology, but the requirement for line-of-sight positioning between the communicating interfaces limits infrared's usefulness. Because Bluetooth uses radio waves, Bluetooth devices can communicate with each other without line-of-sight.

The Bluetooth standard is part of the IEEE 802.15 family of standards for wireless PANs. It was developed by a group of five interested parties who, in 1998, formed the Bluetooth Special Interest Group (SIG) and founded the Bluetooth consortium. Now the consortium has over 2,000 members.

Like WiFi, Bluetooth uses the 2.4 GHz ISM frequency band. But instead of using a wireless NIC, the Bluetooth wireless transceiver and control functions are embedded in a small, low-cost microchip that is more suitable for incorporation into small devices like a mouse or a headset, and has a much lower power requirement than a WiFi NIC. When switched on, Bluetooth devices find each other by transmitting a message which alerts other Bluetooth devices in the vicinity.

Any two Bluetooth-enabled devices can form an ad hoc connection and establish a personal area network (PAN) known as a **piconet** (Figure 16) which can connect together up to eight communicating devices, each being identified by its MAC address. One device in the piconet becomes the master unit and the others act as slaves, responding to 'commands' from the master. The master unit controls all aspects of the communication within the piconet, designating dedicated time slots when each slave can communicate. This prevents slaves from sending data simultaneously.

piconet

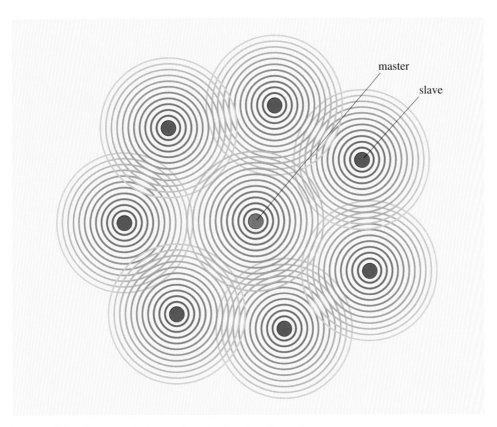

Figure 16 Representation of a Bluetooth piconet

When there is a need for more than eight active devices to form a network, two or more piconets can be connected together into what is known as a **scatternet**. In this arrangement, every piconet must have one master, but a device could be a slave in one piconet and a master in another. Information can then be passed from piconet to piconet under the control of the piconets' master units. Figure 17 shows a scatternet made up of two piconets.

scatternet

Because of the low power output of a Bluetooth transmitter, communication is limited to a range of approximately 10 m, but this distance may be reduced by physical obstructions. Bluetooth's maximum data rate is 1 Mbps but management overheads reduce this to an effective throughput of around 75% – usually quoted as 721 kbps depending on the mode of operation.

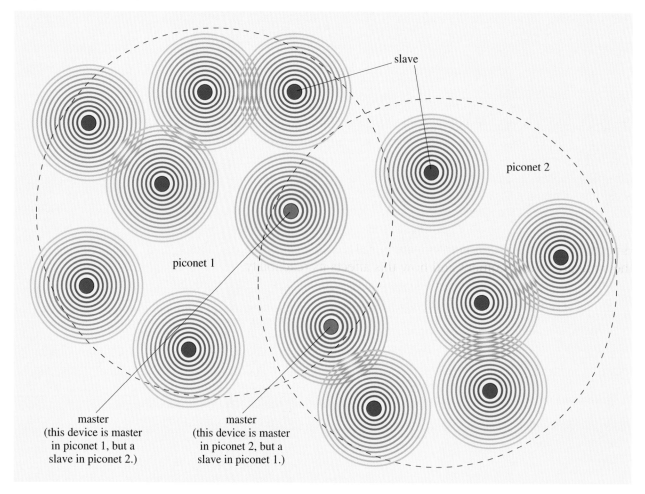

Figure 17 Representation of a Bluetooth scatternet

Activity 19 (self-assessment)

To test your understanding of what you have read so far about Bluetooth, say whether each of the statements below is true or false.

1 Bluetooth devices communicate using infrared.

2 Bluetooth is a technology for use in a PAN.

3 Bluetooth devices do not need a MAC address.

4 There is an upper limit on the number of active devices that can communicate in a piconet.

Comment

The answers are given at the end of this part.

The next study session includes a comparison between WiFi and Bluetooth technologies.

Study Session 5: Comparisons

5.1   Introduction

In many situations, more than one technical solution is possible. It could be that none of them provides a completely ideal solution; each is likely to have its own merits and drawbacks, and often a compromise has to be made. This study session is about comparisons. First I ask you to make a comparison between the two wireless technologies introduced in Study Session 4. This leads to a discussion about competing technologies and some of the issues that will influence the choice of technology for a particular application. I shall also ask you to make a comparison between different ways of presenting information. This leads to a discussion about the structure of a document and how this affects its readability.

5.2   Comparing WiFi and Bluetooth

Activity 20 (self-assessment)

I have used Table 2 to help me make a comparison between WiFi IEEE 802.11g and Bluetooth. Try to complete the empty cells yourself from the information I have given about these two technologies. There may be some cells where the answer is not completely clear cut, but try to give as much information as you can to enable a comparison to be made between the two technologies.

Table 2   Comparison of WiFi IEEE 802.11g and Bluetooth

Characteristic	WiFi	Bluetooth
How transmitted		wireless in the ISM band
Equipment needed	NIC and possibly access point	
Maximum data rate		
Approximate maximum throughput		721 kbps
Methods for sharing the medium	protocols for sharing	
Optimum operating range		
Standards family		
Network structure		piconet or scatternet
Number of nodes supported	depends on equipment manufacturer but limited by minimum useful data rate	

Comment

My answer is given at the end of this part.

As you were working through Activity 20, you will have seen that some of the information needed to complete the table was not clear cut. For example, the WiFi discussion in the previous study session quoted operating ranges of both 30 m and 100 m. It was stated that achievable data rate falls off at distances greater than 30 m, so it was clear that the optimum range is up to 30 m. But the Bluetooth discussion simply stated that range 'is limited to approximately 10 m' and there was no information given on whether data rates are improved at a closer range.

In exercises of this type you may sometimes find it quite difficult to compare like for like because the information may not always be available to you. On occasions you will need to make reasonable compromises, as I did in my answer when I identified 'less than 10 m' as the optimum range for Bluetooth. The point is, for the purposes of my comparison, this would have been sufficient because I can see from the completed table in my answer to Activity 20 (Table 4) that WiFi has a range that is at least three times that of Bluetooth given no physical obstructions.

5.3   Competing technologies

Look again at Table 4. If I simply wanted to connect my computer and my mouse wirelessly, would I use WiFi? If I wanted to connect together six or seven laptop computers so that they could share information with each other in a face-to-face business meeting, would I use Bluetooth? On first analysis both technologies might offer possible solutions for either of these applications (though I suspect that the relatively slow data rate of a Bluetooth network would prove rather restricting in the business meeting). In practice though I wouldn't simply be thinking about the technical specifications such as operating range and throughput; I would need to consider a range of issues such as power requirements, security and reliability, and issues related to the set-up, maintenance and use of the network. Some of these issues are discussed below.

5.3.1   Power requirements

You may remember I started my discussion of wireless technologies in Study Session 4 by reminiscing about my parents' term 'wireless' to describe a device that very clearly needed a cabled connection. It's easy to forget that wireless devices still need a power source to provide them with the energy to operate. For some devices (like my parents' 'wireless') this can be provided by a cabled connection to an electrical power socket. Other devices, like laptop computers and PDAs, are intended to be moved from place to place and not 'tethered' by a cable to an electricity supply. For these, battery power is the answer. Devices with low power requirements mean that small batteries can be used or that operating time can be extended. WiFi is more 'power hungry' than Bluetooth and so will drain a battery much faster.

5.3.2   Security

Because wireless signals travel in free space, they can be picked up by any device in range equipped with a suitable radio receiver. This has implications for the security of data on a wireless network, as it could be accessed by outside devices. Both WiFi and Bluetooth are equipped to address this problem by a combination of authentication and encryption. **Authentication** is a method of controlling access to the network so that only recognised devices are accepted. This can be done using a password or the MAC address of the device. **Encryption** involves scrambling the data in such a way that it becomes extremely difficult for any unauthenticated device to unscramble it. When properly implemented, Bluetooth and the 802.11g WiFi standard provide good, but not perfect, data security.

authentication

encryption

5.3.3   Reliability

In this context I will define reliability as the ability of a technology to perform its intended function, without failure, under stated conditions and for a stated period of time. It is beyond the scope of this course to provide a detailed comparison of the reliability of WiFi and Bluetooth, so here I simply want to alert you to some of the issues. Broadly these are:

- What is the likelihood of data errors being introduced during transmission?
- How well does the technology recover from such errors?
- What is the likelihood of system failure?
- How does the technology perform in terms of availability of service?

Bluetooth and WiFi both operate within the unlicensed ISM band of radio frequencies which is shared by other devices – cordless phones and microwave ovens, for example. Interference from other devices operating at the same or close frequencies is a potential problem as this can introduce transmission errors. So an issue here concerns the resistance of each technology to this kind of interference. In particular, a Bluetooth network could be operating within range of other Bluetooth networks (for example, a Bluetooth headset could be communicating with a mobile phone in the vicinity of a computer sending data to a printer via a Bluetooth link).

> *To see why microwave ovens operate in the ISM band, look back at Figure 6 in Study Session 2. Notice how there is an overlap between the higher frequencies in the radio spectrum and the lower frequencies in the microwave spectrum. This occurs between about 10^9 Hz (1 GHz) and 10^{10} Hz (10 GHz). The ISM frequency band sits around 2.4 GHz.*

5.3.4 Set-up and maintenance

Issues for set-up and maintenance include:

- Cost (what are the costs of setting up and maintaining the technology?)
- Availability of components (are components readily available?)
- Interoperability (will devices from different vendors work together?)
- Continuity of supply (will components still be available for a reasonable period in the future?)

Because of its greater range and complexity, a WiFi network is more expensive to set up and maintain than a Bluetooth network. WiFi and Bluetooth standards are both open, so all devices that follow the standard should interoperate. The open standard is likely to have a positive influence on the take-up of the technology, and consequently on both current and future availability of components and their cost.

5.3.5 Usability

Issues about usability include questions such as:

- How easy is it to install, set up and maintain the technology?
- How easy is it to use?
- What is the quality of product support?'

Again, it is beyond the scope of this course to compare these issues for WiFi and Bluetooth, but points to consider would be how easy it is to access the network and connect to other devices.

5.4 Structuring information

I expect that as you completed the table in Activity 20 you were skipping back and forth between the sections headed 'WiFi' and 'Bluetooth' in Study Session 4. Did you notice that I used a rather different way of presenting my discussion in these two sections? This was quite deliberate, because I want to investigate how these different approaches affect the way you extract information from written material.

I suspect that you may have found it rather easier to search for and identify the information you needed from the WiFi section. In that section I divided my explanation into subsections, giving each a clear heading. Because a number of the headings (e.g. 'Sharing the medium', 'Data rate', 'Operating range', 'Network structure', 'Number of stations') correspond quite closely to the row headings in Table 2, you would have been able to home in on what you wanted. Even where there wasn't such a direct link, the headings themselves provide a strong clue about the content of that subsection (e.g. 'How WiFi stations find each other').

The Bluetooth section is short, and this is why I decided not to use the same section headings that I used for WiFi. I felt this would have

produced a very 'staccato' effect with some subsections only a few words in length. The lack of section headings meant that there were no strong visual cues, and you may have found yourself having to scan the section two or three times to extract what you needed. Even so, I hope you found this to be a fairly easy task because of the way I had structured the information using paragraphs.

Activity 21 (self-assessment)

Examine each of the six paragraphs in Section 4.5 before Activity 19. Try to identify the main theme of each paragraph. (It will help if you number the paragraphs 1 to 6.)

Comment

My answer is given at the end of this part.

While you were working through Activity 21, you might have noticed that some paragraphs included a sentence that didn't seem to fit comfortably with the others. For example, the main topic of Paragraph 3 is the means of transmission and the equipment needed, but the final sentence is a bit at odds with this because it talks about how Bluetooth devices find each other. In my first draft I put this sentence at the beginning of Paragraph 4, but it didn't seem to fit very well there either because Paragraph 4 talks about the piconet structure and how communication is controlled within this network.

I could instead have isolated the sentence into a paragraph on its own, but single-sentence paragraphs work well only in particular situations – such as in pages of notes, in lists in the form of numbered or bulleted points, or in a very few situations when a single-sentence paragraph can be used to emphasise or draw attention to a particular point. So I chose instead to place this information within what I felt was the most closely related paragraph. After reflection Paragraph 3 won by a short head over Paragraph 4.

Activity 22 (exploratory)

Paragraph 6 (of Section 4.5) consists of just two sentences. Do they both fit comfortably together in the paragraph? Could they have been better placed elsewhere?

Comment

Here is my analysis.

The first sentence in paragraph 6 is concerned with range, and what limits the range. The second sentence is about data rate and throughput. Nothing is discussed that links together these two

properties, so they don't fit logically within the same paragraph. However, neither of them would fit comfortably in any of the foregoing paragraphs, and separating them would result in two single-sentence paragraphs. I felt that together they provided an acceptable ending to the Bluetooth section because they 'mopped up' the outstanding points I wanted to make.

On reflection, a better place for the whole of Paragraph 6 would have been after Paragraph 3, because Paragraph 3 ends with a comment about the relatively low power requirement of a Bluetooth transceiver, and Paragraph 6 starts by noting the effect of power output on range. This change of ordering would have provided a good link between the two ideas.

Decisions about headings, sub-headings, grouping of points into paragraphs, and appropriate ordering of points are all concerned with the structure of a document. So are decisions about whether to use tables and numbered or bulleted lists, and where to position any figures used. Good technical explanations need to be carefully structured and clearly presented. A good structure will help the reader to follow the points the author is making and grasp the contents of a document more easily. You will need to think about this when you write your answers to assignments.

As an example of poor structure, look at the text below. It is intended to provide a short introduction to WiFi and Bluetooth technologies and a brief comparison of some of their characteristics.

> WiFi is able to provide a data rate that is at least 10 times faster than Bluetooth, which is generally used for short-range communication between ICT devices such as computers, printers, keyboards, PDAs etc. They both use the 2.4 GHz ISM radio frequency band. Bluetooth's transmission range is typically 10m. Because it uses a small low-power microchip rather than a NIC, Bluetooth is better suited for incorporation into small devices. It enables these devices to communicate without the need for cables linking them together. WiFi uses a network interface card (NIC) to transmit signals. Both WiFi and Bluetooth are defined by a set of standards produced by the IEEE. WiFi and Bluetooth are technologies that provide a means to transmit data wirelessly between devices. WiFi tends to be used in local area networks as an alternative to a wired network. WiFi's range is typically 30 m. ISM stands for 'industrial, scientific and medical'. IEEE stands for 'Institute of Electrical and Electronics Engineers'. PDA stands for 'personal digital assistant'.

If asked to rewrite this so that it is easier to follow, this is how I would approach the task. First I would look to see if I could group the points into a number of main topics. Here's what I found:

- points about differences in the two technologies and why these differences make them suitable for particular applications;

- points that are common to both WiFi and Bluetooth and provide a general introduction to the technologies;

- points about the network interfaces.

Next I would think about ordering, asking questions such as:

- Would the information be better divided into separate paragraphs?

- What would provide a good introduction?

- Do any of the points rely on information that should be given earlier?

Activity 23 (self-assessment)

Using paragraphs but no sub-headings, rewrite the sample text so that it becomes easier for the reader to follow the points made. On the assumption that most of the information is new to the reader, make sure you cover all the information given, ordering and grouping it appropriately. (You don't have to stick to exactly the same wording and sentence structure as the original.)

Comment

My answer is given at the end of this part.

Study Session 6: Smart homes

6.1 Introduction

My discussions of Ethernet, WiFi and Bluetooth have provided you with an introduction to some fundamental principles of wired and wireless networks. This section will build on these general ideas. Up to this point I have been talking in rather general terms about devices communicating with each other, but in this and the next study session I am going to focus on two specific situations where this happens. The first of these is a 'smart home', which I will discuss in this study session; the second is a system of identity tagging, known as RFID, which I will cover in Study Session 7.

To open the smart-home discussion, here is a short extract from *The Road Ahead* written by Bill Gates in 1995. In it he talks about a house he was having built for himself.

Where you see a series of three dots (called an ellipsis) enclosed in square brackets, this indicates that part of the original text has been omitted from the quotation.

> When you come in, you'll be presented with an electronic pin to clip to your clothes. The pin will connect you up to the electronic services of the house. [...]
>
> The electronic pin you wear will tell the house who and where you are, and the house will use this information to try to meet and even anticipate your needs – all as unobtrusively as possible. [...] When it's dark outside, the pin will cause a zone of light to move with you through the house. Unoccupied rooms will be unlit. As you walk down a hallway, you might not notice the lights ahead of you gradually coming up to full brightness and the lights behind you fading. Music will move with you too. It will seem to be everywhere, although in fact people in other parts of the house will be hearing entirely different music or nothing at all. If you get a phone call, only the handset nearest you will ring.
>
> Gates, W. (1995)

What Gates is describing here is a 'smart' home, where all the important electrical devices and services are linked together by a communication network so that they can be monitored and controlled automatically or remotely. Smart homes are also referred to as 'automated homes' and sometimes 'networked homes' (though the term 'networked home' is more likely to refer to a home with a network that connects together entertainment devices such as televisions and DVD players with computers, and often includes an internet link).

6.2 Devices in the home

Activity 24 (exploratory)

Take a mental 'walkthrough' of a typical morning in your own home, making a note of all the events and activities that involve electrical devices.

Comment

My imagined day starts even before I wake up, when the domestic heating system comes on and my alarm clock switches on the radio. If it's winter time I switch on my bedroom light (how nice instead to have a more natural awakening by my bedroom lights coming on at a low level and gradually increasing to full brightness.) I go to the bathroom, take a shower (adjusting the temperature to my own preference) then make coffee and toast in the kitchen. I burn the toast and the smoke alarm sounds. I go into the living room and use a remote control to switch on the TV for the morning news. Then I go upstairs and dry my hair. On a good day I might have time to run the vacuum cleaner over the carpets, load and switch on the washing machine or preset the oven so that the casserole I prepared the night before will be cooked and ready to eat on my return.

Activity 25 (exploratory)

Which of the devices I mentioned in my answer to Activity 24 would you say were concerned with monitoring and controlling?

Comment

The devices that control my central heating monitor the temperature of the air and hot water, and control the boiler accordingly. My alarm clock monitors the time and controls the switching on (and off) of the radio. The smoke alarm monitors certain chemicals in the air and activates an alarm when these rise above a critical level. If I have one of the more expensive models of toaster, it might monitor the dryness of the bread and control the toasting time to prevent burning. My TV can be controlled with a remote device; the washing machine and oven are both operated by some kind of program controller.

6.3 Devices for automatic control

Sensors and actuators were mentioned in the introduction to the article *Networked microsensors and the end of the world as we know it* that you read in Study Session 1. **Sensors** are devices that measure some

sensor

actuator

physical property – for example, temperature, electrical resistance, motion – and provide an output in a form that can be interpreted and communicated. **Actuators** are devices that take some kind of action in response to a signal – examples include an electric motor or an electrically controlled valve.

Activity 26 (exploratory)

Try to think of at least one example of a sensor and one example of an actuator in use in your own home.

Comment

For examples of a sensor I thought of the PIR (passive infrared) detector used to trigger a security light outside my house, the smoke detectors embedded in my smoke alarms, the temperature sensors in my central heating and hot water system, and the device in my electric kettle that senses when the water is boiling. Some of these devices are intrinsically coupled to an actuator.

For examples of an actuator I thought about the electrically operated valves that control the flow of water into my washing machine and dishwasher, the release mechanism on my washing machine door, the loudspeakers on my audio system (where the speaker cone moves in response to an electrical signal). I also thought about the little hammer that used to strike the bell on intruder alarms and doorbells – but I don't have any of these.

6.4   Signal accuracy

In the article *Networked Microsensors and the end of the world as we know it* the author talks about sensors being able to link the 'world of events' with the 'electronic world of computers, processes and storage devices [...] by integrating analogue sensing with digital processing [...]' (Shepherd, 2003).

In the physical world, events usually take place as an ever-changing continuum. Time passes, the seasons change, temperatures fluctuate and water reservoirs fill and drain. All these happen as infinitesimally small changes in a continuum of change. But using ICTs to capture, store and manipulate data about these kinds of physical event requires a process of periodic sampling and then converting the sampled values into digital information. In Part 2, Study Session 6 you were led through this process in the context of speech signals, but similar principles apply generally (not just to speech) when signals are converted from analogue to digital. The amount of digital information required to represent the original analogue signal depends on how close the representation needs to be.

This will determine the number of samples needed and the number of quantisation levels.

Many control and monitoring applications don't require a high degree of accuracy. For example – if I wanted to provide just enough heat to prevent water from freezing in a tank I'd probably want a system that would provide some heat when the temperature fell to about 3 °C or 4 °C, but a variation of a degree or so above or below this would probably be adequate. (In practice, the position of the sensor in this example would also be very important because the temperature of a tank of water can vary across its volume.)

6.5   Smart home networks

Some devices in a smart home may need to communicate information about the environment (for example, information about light, heat, humidity, sound, movement, water levels, etc.). They may also need to communicate to:

- give information about their state (for example, activated, deactivated, faulty);
- give temporal information (for example clock time, lapsed time, delays);
- instruct, interrogate or acknowledge another device.

Such information can generally be represented with a few tens of bits of data. This is extremely small compared to the quantity of data needed to represent, say, a voice signal, an image, or a few seconds of video. Because of this the data rate requirement of a smart home's networks is extremely low – a fraction of the capability of the network technologies you met earlier (Ethernet, WiFi and Bluetooth).

Many monitoring and control devices used in the home need to be active only for short periods, with relatively long periods of inactivity in between. (In the world of electronic communications 'long periods' could refer to fractions of a second.) For example, a device may need to check only periodically to see if its controller has a message for it, and the rest of the time it can 'sleep'. The ratio of activity to inactivity is known as a **duty cycle** and is generally expressed as a percentage. As an example, I'll examine a device that typically connects to a network and transmits for 15 milliseconds in every second. (A millisecond is 1/1000th of a second and is indicated by the symbol ms – m for 'milli' and s for 'second'.) First I need to express 15 milliseconds in seconds:

duty cycle

$$15 \text{ ms} = \frac{15}{1000} \text{ s} = 0.015 \text{ s}$$

Next I need to express 0.015 seconds as a percentage of 1 second:

$$\frac{0.015}{1} \times 100 = 1.5\%$$

So in this particular example, the device has a typical duty cycle of 1.5%. That is, it is active for only about 1.5% of the time.

Activity 27 (self-assessment)

Calculate the duty cycle of a device that typically connects to a network and transmits for 20 ms in every 0.5 s.

Comment

The answer is given at the end of this part

Monitoring and control devices used in the home also tend to be tolerant of delays between the sending of a message and a response. In my earlier example of the water tank, a delay of a few seconds between the water temperature falling to the trigger point and the heater switching on would be quite acceptable. (Again, in the world of electronic communications 'long' delays can be measured in terms of milliseconds.)

So, a typical device used in a smart home network has three characteristics that result in very low data-rate requirements. These are:

- the small quantity of data needed to represent the signal;
- the low duty cycle;
- the tolerance to delay.

Activity 28 (exploratory)

Would either Bluetooth or WiFi provide suitable candidates for a 'smart home' wireless network?

Comment

Although Bluetooth and WiFi operate at data rates far in excess of the requirement, neither would provide good solutions for a smart home network. WiFi devices need some kind of NIC which would make them bulky, and WiFi is 'energy hungry'. For devices (such as a smoke alarm) that rely on battery power, this could lead to frequent battery changing. Although power consumption is less of a problem with Bluetooth (because of its lower energy requirements), it would nevertheless be significant in a multi-device installation. Furthermore, Bluetooth has an operating range of up to only 10 m and this is reduced in situations where there are physical barriers such as walls and windows.

There are a number of wireless technologies specifically designed for home automation networks. In the next section I'm going to introduce one that is, at the time of writing, still in its development stage with no commercial products available on the market. I've chosen it because it looks likely to become a key player in smart home technology – but perhaps you will be in a better position to judge whether this prediction has come true. The system is called ZigBee.

6.6   ZigBee

Development of the ZigBee standard is the result of a group of interested parties coming together to form the ZigBee Alliance. When approved it will be an open standard sitting within a subset of the IEEE 802.15.4 low-data wireless standard. At the outset ZigBee was designed specifically for networks set up for the purposes of monitoring and control. Two of the major development aims were that it should be low cost (so that it is cheap to install and maintain), and low power (for long battery life). ZigBee technology exploits the low duty-cycle characteristics and low data-rate requirements of the devices it serves. The technology enables devices to enter a 'sleep' state when they are inactive. In this state they consume very little power and this means that batteries can have extremely long lives. (I've seen claims of up to 10 years.) Table 3 summarises the key characteristics of ZigBee.

Table 3   Characteristics of the ZigBee wireless system

Characteristic	
How transmitted	radio transmission in 2.4 GHz to 2.483 GHz ISM frequency band
Equipment needed	transceiver, processor, small amount of memory
Maximum data rate	250 kbps
Maximum throughput	over 200 kbps
Method for sharing the medium	managed by a network coordinator device
Operating range	up to approximately 70 m indoors, but increased range possible using mesh rather than star topology
Standards family	IEEE 802.15 family of PAN standards
Network structure	star or mesh type
Number of nodes supported	theoretical maximum of 65,536

ZigBee can also operate in two other frequency bands, providing lower data rates.

Each ZigBee network must include a network coordinator. This device is responsible for network set-up and message routing, as well as managing data communications.

The transceiver, processor and memory can be built together into a microchip. Because of the low energy requirements of the device, quite small batteries can power it for a convenient period of time. This means that ZigBee can be incorporated into many of the home-control and remote sensing devices previously discussed, without significantly increasing their size.

Activity 29 (exploratory)

When operating in a mesh topology, explain how this structure contributes to the reliability of a ZigBee network. Why might reliability be an important consideration in a smart home network?

Comment

A mesh structure implies data routing capabilities, so if a node or link fails it could be possible to find an alternative route. In a smart home network, reliability is an important consideration. For example, you could be depending on a signal from a smoke alarm to trigger a sprinkler system.

6.7   Issues

The extract from *The Road Ahead* quoted at the beginning of this Study Session presents a very rosy picture of life in a smart home. So what are the implications of the deployment of smart home technology? Does it provide us with a utopian environment that can bring only benefits? Or does the technology pose threats and dangers too? These questions are considered below.

6.7.1   Benefits

I can think of a number of possible benefits – apart from the obvious one about relieving me of the tedium of performing a lot of routine tasks. The first one I thought about was the potential saving in energy the technology could bring – for instance by switching off devices (TV, radio, hifi, heaters, lights) when there's no one there to use them.

The second advantage I thought about was the potential for independence that smart home technology could provide for the elderly or infirm – a key consideration in an ageing society. As well as automating routine tasks, devices could feed information back to a monitoring system so that if, for example, a kettle hasn't been used or a door opened for some time, carers are alerted to a potential problem.

I also thought about the potential it could provide for me to monitor and control my home remotely. If I found I was going to be unexpectedly late returning home I could arrange for curtains or blinds to be drawn, a light to be switched on to deter intruders, and the heating cycle to be delayed. I could also ask my house to report certain conditions to me when I was away – burst pipes, equipment failures or overheating appliances, for example. I wondered whether insurance companies might charge lower premiums for household insurance if such monitoring systems were in place. I also wondered whether the ability to monitor buildings from a remote location might lead to crime reduction.

With suitably placed closed-circuit TV cameras, a smart home network could help parents keep an eye on children in different rooms. Indeed, with a smart home network linked to the internet, parents could also monitor older children at home on their own.

6.7.2 Drawbacks

One of the issues I thought about was privacy. How would the elderly or infirm feel about being monitored in their own homes? How would teenage children at home feel about being under the constant eye of their parents?

I also thought about security. Would it be possible for a hacker to break into my smart home network – possibly to disable intruder alarms and open doors to allow themselves entry? A malicious hacker might also alter control settings to cause havoc – turning on or off devices in a way that could put my home at risk, or increase my service charges.

Another concern about the technology is what happens if it goes wrong. In the case of a power failure there would need to be safeguards to ensure that I could manually override the controls without too much difficulty (for example I would need to be able to open the doors or windows) and to ensure that my control settings were retained.

6.8 The personalised home

In the extract from *The Road Ahead* that I quoted at the beginning of this study session, Gates makes reference to 'an electronic pin to clip to your clothes'. This pin appears to have the ability to communicate to the network so that its wearer can be identified and located. The information can then be used to provide a personal environment for the wearer. The next study session introduces you to a technology that can provide the kind of pin that Gates refers to.

Study Session 7: RFID

7.1 Introduction

For part of this study session you will need to work online.

This study session continues with the theme of networked devices by looking at a system of electronic tagging known as Radio Frequency Identity (RFID). In this system, an electronic tag is attached to an object (for example, the pin described in the *The Road Ahead* extract in the previous study session) and an RFID reader is used to interrogate the tag wirelessly and receive information stored on it. I am using the word 'interrogate' here because the reader sends out a signal and the tag responds with its data in a question-and-answer type of exchange. The signals passing between the tag and the reader are radio frequency signals – hence the description 'RFID' to describe this type of technology.

At its simplest level, the information held on the tag is an identity code, which may be used as a reference to information stored in a database. The RFID reader transmits the tag's information to a host computer for processing. Or the tag could store information about the object it is attached to – for example, its weight, price, date of manufacture, etc.

At this point in your studies you will have sufficient background knowledge about networks and communication systems to enable you to do a little of your own research. In a fast-moving field like ICTs, the Web provides a key resource for keeping yourself updated on new developments. Activities in this and the next study session will provide you with opportunities to search for and identify relevant information from third-party sources and to develop the skill of presenting, in your own words, the information you find.

'Third party' is a term borrowed from the legal profession in the context of contracts between two parties – for example a policyholder and an insurance company. The policyholder is referred to as the first party, the insurance company as the second party and anyone else as the third party. In the context of your learning 'contract' with The Open University, you are the first party, The Open University is the second party and anyone else is the third party. So when I refer to 'third-party sources' I am referring to any sources originating elsewhere.

7.2   RFID

The technology behind RFID is relatively straightforward and has been in use in some form for many years. You may have even used it yourself or seen it in use – for example in a 'proximity card' entry system in buildings, and in pet identification where a microchip is inserted just below an animal's skin. But you are likely to hear a lot more about it in the future and increasingly to see it deployed. This is because, at the time of writing (early 2005), the technology is receiving a strong push from some large retail companies such as Wal-Mart, Tesco and Marks & Spencer. They are investigating its deployment in their supply chain, where they hope it will provide a low-cost means of tracking stock items from manufacturer through to customer.

By now you will be familiar with the idea that devices in a network need some unique identity so that they can be addressed unambiguously. But what if everything in the world could be tagged with a unique identity: every item on every supermarket shelf; every item you wear or carry with you; every item in your home and workplace? And what if we could use ICTs to help us to communicate information about these uniquely identified objects? Far from being a blip on the technical horizon, elements of such a system are already with us and we have the potential to create 'an internet of everything'. That is, we have the ability to track objects, record and update information about them, and make all this accessible through a global network. What are the possibilities provided by this technology, and what are the implications?

The idea of identifying objects isn't new. The method of barcode identity has been in commercial use since the mid-1970s. A barcode can identify an item as one of a particular type of product – for example, a 100 g jar of Café Direct coffee. But it can't identify an item individually and uniquely – for example, the two-hundred-and-thirtieth 100 g jar of Café Direct coffee to roll off the production line on the 15th July 2005. Neither can it provide access to other information like the length of time it was stored in the warehouse, the name of the carriers who shipped it to the supermarket, the length of time it has been displayed on the shelf, and recycling information about the bottle.

Another limitation of an optical scanning system is that the scanner and barcode have to be within line-of-sight of each other, and correct recognition is dependent on the optical clarity of both of them. How many times have you been in a supermarket queue and watched the checkout staff making several attempts to scan a barcode, only to end up entering the number manually into the checkout system? RFID tags can suffer some damage and still be read, they'll work in environments that are hot and dirty, they don't require line-of-sight so can still be read through obstructions like packaging and pallets, and some tags can be read from distances of several tens of metres.

7.3 RFID technology

There are three main components in an RFID system:

- A tag (consisting of electronic circuitry and an antenna), which acts as a data store and wireless **transponder**. (A transponder is a device that automatically sends a signal in response to interrogation from another device.)

transponder

- A reader (consisting of electronic circuitry and an antenna), which acts as a controller unit and transceiver. (In Study Session 2 you were introduced to the term 'transceiver' – a device that transmits and receives signals.)

- A host computer system that processes and manages the information it receives from the reader.

Figure 18 illustrates the relationship between these components.

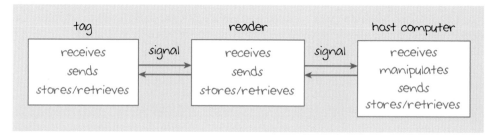

Figure 18   Representation of a simple RFID system

A reader can interrogate multiple tags and send the data from each to a host computer, which in turn could be connected through a network to other computers in an RFID system (Figure 19). In this way, the data from a tag on an item could be recorded as it travels from the manufacturer, to the warehouse, through the distribution and transport networks, to the retailer, to the point-of-sale terminal and even beyond. The data could be stored on a central database to provide a complete history of the item.

7.4 RFID tags

An RFID tag consists of a microchip and an antenna and some kind of encapsulation, such as epoxy resin, to bind the two together and protect them. Tags come in a variety of shapes and sizes (Figure 20), and are generally one of two main types: active or passive. You'll be learning more about these later.

In the next activity I shall be asking you to read three extracts that I've taken from different websites. These extracts are printed in the following three boxes. When you've read the extracts I shall ask you to write a short comparison of active tags and passive tags. It would be tempting,

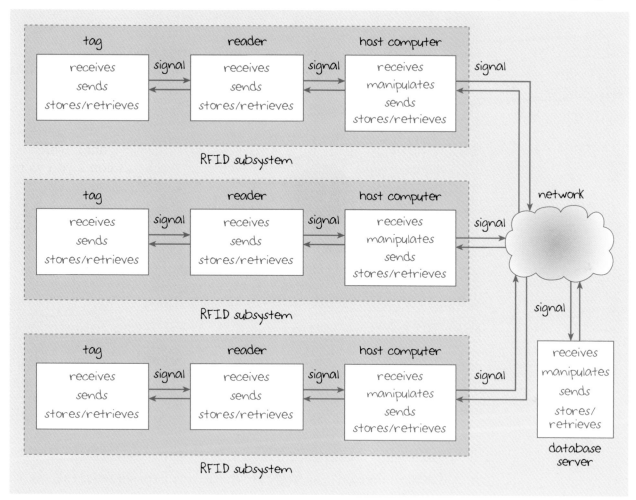

Figure 19 Representation of a simple networked RFID system

and very easy, to simply copy selected parts of the extracts and 'stitch' them together for your own explanation. It's even harder to resist this when working with electronic sources directly from the Web because of the ease of 'cut and paste'. However, unless the quoted text is properly indicated and referenced, using other people's work like this is plagiarism (that is, copying someone else's work and passing it off as your own), and is not acceptable. Neither is lightly paraphrasing the work of others. Paraphrasing is the act of restating, using different words, what someone else has said. Light paraphrasing means that the original words or structure are hardly changed.

Using your own words will help you to clarify and demonstrate your own understanding but, when you are working with other people's ideas, it can be quite difficult to 'forget' the words they have used and to

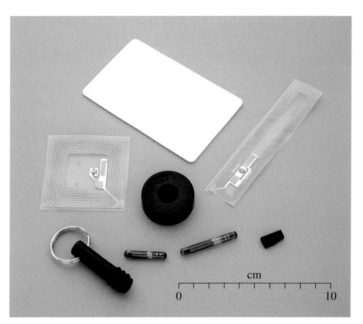

Figure 20 Examples of RFID tags

resist the temptation to 'borrow' some of their sentences or part sentences and general structure. Here's how I approach the task:

1 I quickly skim through the document to get a feel for the topic and to identify the main points.

2 I review the task I'm attempting so that I can focus on what is needed and avoid irrelevant information.

3 I reread the document slowly (or the parts I have identified as relevant), making notes either electronically or on a piece of paper as I go along. Usually these notes are just keywords, spray diagrams or short phrases. If I'm trying to make a comparison between two or more things, my notes might be in the form of lists or a rough table. I try never to repeat parts or whole sentences from the source document.

4 I put the source documents out of sight and attempt a first draft of my own document. This usually reveals any 'holes' or areas of confusion I have, and I make a note of these. But at this point I do have some text that is essentially my own words and structure.

5 I go back to the source document to see if I can fill the gaps and clarify my understanding. Sometimes I find that the source document doesn't give me all the information I need and I might need to look elsewhere. In this way I can build my own knowledge much more firmly than when I'm simply being 'fed' the information. (But in this first exercise I'm not going to ask you to look for other sources.)

Activity 30 (exploratory)

Read the extracts in the following three boxes. Using the information they contain, make notes about the main differences between active and passive RFID tags. You will get more out of this exercise if you make a serious attempt to do this before reading my answer.

Extract from 'What is Radio Frequency Identity (RFID)?'

RFID tags are categorised as either active or passive. Active RFID tags are powered by an internal battery and are typically read/write, i.e., tag data can be rewritten and/or modified. An active tag's memory size varies according to application requirements; some systems operate with up to 1 MB of memory. In a typical read/write RFID work-in-process system, a tag might give a machine a set of instructions, and the machine would then report its performance to the tag. This encoded data would then become part of the tagged part's history. The battery-supplied power of an active tag generally gives it a longer read range. The trade off is greater size, greater cost, and a limited operational life (which may yield a maximum of 10 years, depending upon operating temperatures and battery type).

Passive RFID tags operate without a separate external power source and obtain operating power generated from the reader. Passive tags are consequently much lighter than active tags, less expensive, and offer a virtually unlimited operational lifetime. The trade off is that they have shorter read ranges than active tags and require a higher-powered reader. Read-only tags are typically passive and are programmed with a unique set of data (usually 32 to 128 bits) that cannot be modified. Read-only tags most often operate as a license plate into a database, in the same way as linear barcodes reference a database containing modifiable product-specific information.

RFID systems are also distinguished by their frequency ranges. Low-frequency (30 kHz to 500 kHz) systems have short reading ranges and lower system costs. They are most commonly used in security access, asset tracking, and animal identification applications. High-frequency (850 MHz to 950 MHz and 2.4 GHz to 2.5 GHz) systems, offering long read ranges (greater than 90 feet) and high reading speeds, are used for such applications as railroad car tracking and automated toll collection. However, the higher performance of high-frequency RFID systems incurs higher system costs.

AIM (n.d.)

'n.d.' stands for 'no date'. It indicates that it wasn't possible to ascertain the date when the quoted extract was written.

Extract from 'The Hidden Secret of the 5 Cent RFID Tag'

At the most basic level, there are two types of RFID tags, passive and active. Passive tags have no power and have to use the radio frequency (RF) field from the reader to transmit their signal from 1–10 feet, depending on the frequency. Active tags use their on-board power to transmit their signal hundreds of feet.

The simplest passive tags have their data burned permanently into the tag when it is made, and some passive tags can have their data rewritten many times. Active tags, on the other hand, can power random access memory (RAM), and typical tags store 32,000 bytes of data. Active tags can also power sensors that detect things like temperature or humidity.

Palmer M. (2004)

Extract from 'How RFID Works'

An active tag is powered by an internal battery, which generally gives it a longer read range than passive tags, which obtain operating power from the reader. Active tags are also usually read/write in comparison with typically read-only passive tags. While active tags can operate with up to 1 MB of memory compared to the 32–128 bits of passive tags, the former are larger, heavier and more expensive than passive tags, which offer a virtually unlimited operating existence in contrast with a maximum active tag lifetime of 10 years. In addition to the lesser memory size, passive tags also have shorter reading ranges and require readers with higher power than those used with active tags. RFID systems are also distinguished by their frequency ranges. Low-frequency (30 kHz to 500 kHz) systems have short reading ranges and lower system costs. They are most commonly used in security access, asset tracking, and animal identification applications. High-frequency (850 MHz to 950 MHz and 2.4 GHz to 2.5 GHz) systems, offering long read ranges (greater than 90 feet) and high reading speeds, are used for such applications as railroad car tracking and automated toll collection. However, the higher performance of high-frequency RFID systems incurs higher system costs.

The Mannings Group (n.d.)

Comment

My initial scan of the three extracts identified a number of clear differences between active and passive tags. So I decided to start by making notes in the form of a simple table, shown as Figure 21 below.

Attribute	Tag type	
	Active	Passive
power source	internal battery	draws power from reader
typical lifespan	10 years max	unlimited
typical capability	read/write	read only
read range	~ 100 ft	1 - 10 ft
typical memory size	1 Mbyte	32 - 128 bits
physical size	> passive	< active
weight	> passive	< active
cost	> passive	< active
reader power	< passive	> active

> means 'greater than'
< means 'less than'
~ means 'approximately'

Figure 21 RFID Tag types

Don't worry if you weren't able to identify quite as many differences as I did, but I hope you got the main ones about power source, lifespan, range and physical size.

The extracts also gave information about the characteristics of tags operating at different frequency ranges. I couldn't cross reference this directly to active or passive tags, so this would be something requiring further investigation.

I hope you also spotted that the information about frequency given in the first and third extracts was identical. This highlights an important point about web sources: very often they are plagiarised work themselves! In this case, one could be copied from the other, or they may have both taken the same section from yet another source. As an experiment, the next time you are connected to the internet you could try entering a portion of the plagiarised section into a Google search – for example "higher performance of high-frequency RFID systems incurs higher system costs" – and see how many 'hits' are returned. (You must include the quotation marks because this forces Google to search for an exact phrase match.) When I tried, the search returned 64 sites!

It's easy to see how inaccurate information could proliferate on the Web in this way. The moral of the story here is, just because you see the same information repeated on various websites you cannot automatically

assume it is accurate. You need to judge this against the authority of the sources. However, in this particular case, the source of the extract is AIM (Automatic Identification Manufacturers), the trade association for the Automatic Identification and Data Capture Industry, so it is safe to assume that the information they publish is reliable.

Activity 31 (self-assessment)

Use your notes from Activity 30 to write, in your own words, a short summary of the differences between active and passive RFID tags. You'll probably be able to do this using no more than 150 words. (Don't worry if your word count isn't close to this – at this stage, using your own words is more important than keeping close to the suggested length.) When you have finished, check back to the original source documents and make sure that your text is sufficiently different for it to be truly your own words.

Again, you'll get more out of this exercise if you make a serious attempt to produce your own answer before reading mine.

Comment

My answer is given at the end of this part.

The next activity stays with the theme of RFID tags but gives you an opportunity to do a little research for yourself. You will need to work online for this activity.

Activity 32 (exploratory)

What is the smallest RFID tag currently available? Use the Web to see what you can come up with but don't spend longer than 10 minutes on this activity. (Hint: using 'smallest RFID tag' as the search term worked for me.)

Comment

When I did my research at the time of writing (early 2005) the smallest tag I could find in commercial use measured 0.4 x 0.4 mm and was 'thinner than a sheet of paper' (Hecht and Hecht, 2004). But I did find reference to a prototype measuring 0.25 x 0.25 mm (RFID News, 2004). Although I wasn't searching for anything about the size of RFID readers, I also stumbled across a reference to an RFID reader measuring 1 inch in diameter by 0.1 inch thick (Hecht and Hecht, 2004), and this seemed relevant to privacy issues because of the ease of hiding small readers so that tags can be read covertly.

When you were doing Activity 27 you probably encountered the same problem as I did: that is, ascertaining the date of the web source. Sometimes it just isn't possible to find out when the article was written. When I'm looking for recent information I click on the 'Advanced search' facility in Google (Figure 22) and set the date parameter to 'past 3 months' (Figure 23). This will filter out some of the older sites, but still offers no real assurance that the information is current because even a slight modification of the page during the selected period means it will be included in the search results. So you can never be absolutely sure that what you are looking at is recent, but you can make some reasonable judgements by considering the authority of the source and looking at what else is around at the time.

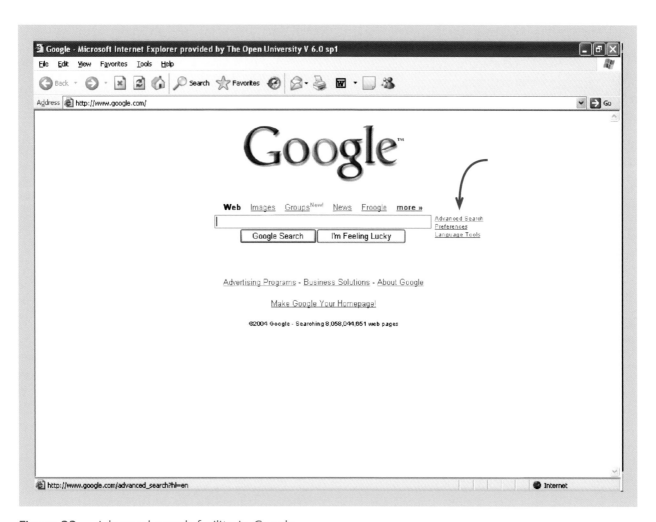

Figure 22   Advanced search facility in Google

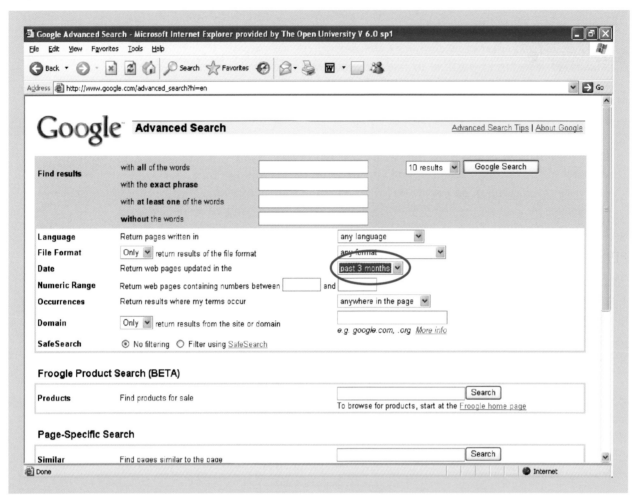

Figure 23 Setting the date parameter in Google

The next (final) study session in Block 2 continues your study of RFID tags by looking at some of their uses.

Study Session 8: Using RFID, and epilogue

8.1 Introduction

You will need to work online for the first activity in this study session.

The first part of this session continues with the work started in Study Session 7. Here you will build on your research to look at some recent applications of RFID and some of the issues surrounding its deployment.

The second part will help you review your experience of studying Part 3 of this block and your learning process during the various parts of Block 2.

8.2 RFID applications

As I pointed out in Study Session 7, the driving force for RFID development is coming from major retailers who want to track goods as they travel through the supply chain. Their purpose is to reduce the manual checking necessary, thereby cutting down on labour costs and reducing human error.

At the time of writing the cost of an RFID tag means that it is only economically viable to tag things like pallets, cases and high-value goods. We are not yet at the point where every tin of baked beans could be tagged. But as the price of an RFID tag drops and issues surrounding standards are clarified, RFID deployment is likely to become more widespread. As I mentioned earlier, the technology is already in use in the retail sector. Marks & Spencer has carried out trials of individual item tagging (men's suits, shirts and ties) in some of its London stores, the UK supermarket giant Tesco has trialled the tagging of razor blades and DVDs, and in Wal-Mart's Dallas store in the USA, printers and scanners have been tracked using RFID tags in their packaging. A Wal-Mart directive to its top 100 suppliers required them to use RFID tags on all pallets and cases entering the supply chain from January 2005.

Outside the retail sector there are some interesting uses for RFID tagging. When I was researching I saw reports of developments on diverse uses, among which were:

- RFID tags inserted under the skin of clubbers in a Barcelona night spot to act as an entry card and to provide access to a debit account for bar bills (Losowsky, 2004);

- RFID tags attached to library books, to assist in record keeping and shelf checking, reduce check-out overheads and prevent theft (Young, 2004);

- RFID tags embedded in casino gambling chips to protect against fraud and money laundering (Hecht, 2004);

- RFID tags to be incorporated in the labels of certain medicine bottles to deter counterfeiting (Information Week, 2004);

- Development of RFID tags which can be incorporated into banknotes to counteract money laundering and counterfeiting (Williams, 2003).

Activity 33 (exploratory)

Use the Web to update yourself on some of the latest developments in RFID systems. (Hint: I used 'RFID news' as my search term in Google.) Visit two or three sites, pick one item you find interesting and make some brief notes about it. Then write about 200 words summarising the article and explaining why you found it particularly interesting. Make sure you include the date of the news item and the URL of the website where the information appeared.

Comment

Of course, I can't predict what RFID developments might be in the news at the time you conduct your research. So my comments are restricted to what I found myself when I did some research in early 2005.

These are the sites I visited:

RFID News site (http://www.rfidnews.org/)

RFID Gazette (http://www.rfidgazette.org/)

RFID Journal (http://www.rfidjournal.com/)

On the 'RFID journal' site some of the news articles were restricted to subscribers only so I couldn't access all of them.

Although my search revealed many news items that had only been posted on the day or within a week of my search, the one that interested me the most wasn't all that recent. It was from RFID News and was dated 10 June 2004. (The URL was http://www.rfidnews.org/news/2004/06/10/rfidenabled-license-plates-to-identify-uk-vehicles/, this link can be found in resources on the T175 website.)

Here is my summary and explanation of why I found this particular article interesting:

The article was about a pilot project (the e-Plates project) to embed active RFID tags in the licence plates of UK vehicles. The tags hold an encrypted ID number which can be matched to

vehicle details held in a central database. The RFID readers can be fixed or mobile and can read tags travelling at speeds of up to 320 kilometres per hour and at distances of up to 100 metres. Unlike camera systems for reading licence plates, the RFID tags can be read in any weather conditions and through dirt on the plate. If anyone tries to remove the tag, the plate will shatter.

What really interested me about this site were the readers' comments at the end and the issues they raised. Some readers were in favour of such a system, saying that it would help with tracking stolen vehicles and would make the payment of road tolls much easier. Others were concerned that the technology would be used for detecting speeding violations and collecting fines, and about privacy issues arising from the location data that would be stored. One person expressed worries that the encrypted signal could somehow be recorded and played back later.

In case this is helpful, the notes I made whilst reading the article are shown in Figure 24.

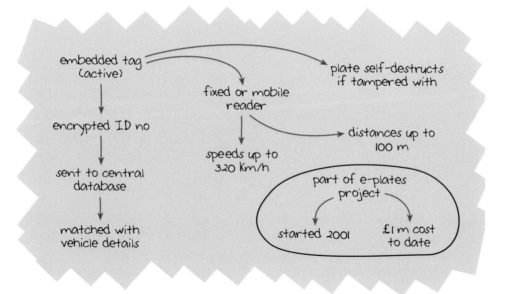

Figure 24   Notes for Activity 33

8.3   Issues

As you've seen, RFID tags can be very small devices – certainly small enough to be inserted unobtrusively under the skin or thin enough to be incorporated into a paper label. Their size (both current and potential), coupled with the expected drop in the cost of RFID tags, means that the technology is likely to find its way into many aspects of our lives. You don't have to search far on the Web to find ideas of how RFID tags might be used in the future. I used a Google search and

entered the name of a selection of common objects, followed by 'RFID' and in almost all cases I found something relevant. Here are the objects I tried: clothes; washing machine; fridge; car; wristwatch. Here are examples of some of the applications I found:

- washing machines that read an RFID tag embedded in clothes and adjust the wash cycle to suit the fabric;
- fridges that read RFID tags on food packaging and alert you when the 'use by' date is reached;
- wristwatches that incorporate a miniature RFID reader and display tag information on a tiny screen.

It's easy to see how the technology can increase the potential for networked living. If you connect strategically placed readers into a smart home network you have the potential to track anything anywhere – including people.

People can be tracked by what they wear and carry and this raises a number of privacy concerns. Some of these concerns relate to the use of RFID tags in the retail supply chain and how we might be tracked by the tags on goods we purchase – tracked not only within the store but outside too. Tags that aren't removed at the point of sale (whether because they are embedded in a product or because they simply aren't removed at the check-out) have the potential to continue to release information about the product they are associated with. Imagine someone sitting next to you on the train being able to identify the entire contents of your bag and pockets – and all without your knowledge!

You will also have seen from my comment on Activity 33 how RFID tags can be used to police particular activities like driving a car. The potential to embed RFID tags into passports and driving licences is seen by many people as a further erosion of personal liberties.

I've already mentioned that clubbers have used subcutaneous (meaning 'under the skin') RFID tags. There are proposals to tag hospital patients in the same way with a unique ID that can be linked to a database containing details of things like blood type, drugs to be administered, dietary requirements, etc. This raises issues about security: could someone maliciously alter the data with disastrous consequences (such as the administration of a fatal dose of medicine)?

8.4   Summary of Block 2 Part 3

In this part of Block 2, the emphasis has been on devices communicating with each other in networks. You were introduced to some general principles about signals and networks, and the differences between wired and wireless networks. You met some of the network technologies in common use (Ethernet, WiFi and Bluetooth), before looking more closely at specific applications (smart homes, RFID

systems) for networked devices. But we have barely had time to scratch the surface of what these technologies offer or the issues they raise.

In the article you looked at in Study Session 1 (*Networked microsensors and the end of the world as we know it*) Shepherd talked about small, powerful devices, linked into networks, that can be used to monitor and control aspects of our environment. He talked about the advantages this can bring to society, and the concerns about the loss of personal privacy that the use of such systems may bring. I hope your study of this part of Block 2 has provided you with some insights into what he was referring to, and an awareness of the huge potential – both enabling and restricting – that these technologies offer.

I hope also that you are feeling more practised in using the Web to find your own information about technologies that are new to you, and more confident about being able to identify reliable resources, extract relevant information and present it in your own words.

8.5   Epilogue

As you worked through Block 2 you have used a variety of media in your studies. Parts 1 and 2 were computer-based, so they were able to incorporate computer animations and online resources in the teaching materials. Part 3 was designed to be print-based and I have deliberately kept computer use to a minimum.

In this final section, I would like you to review the influence of the different media on your learning experience. What worked best for you and why? What particular problems arose through the use of the different media? What strategies could you develop to overcome these problems?

To get you started on this, here are some examples of the sort of benefits and drawbacks that I've heard discussed in relation to different learning media.

Computer-based study means you are 'tethered' to your computer, and for many people this restricts the opportunities for study. But it does provide access to rich and varied resources. Computer animations and video clips can help to demonstrate a concept more clearly than text or diagrams. Access to websites gives learners more independence and provides different views – but it can be distracting and difficult to know when to stop. It's easy to 'over research' a topic and end up with too much material to cope with. Some people find it difficult to read and take notes when working from a computer screen and end up printing out quantities of information.

Print-based learning material is portable, so it's possible to keep study materials close at hand and find study opportunities at odd times – for example, on the train, during a lunch break, in waiting rooms. But the materials can be easily mislaid and difficult to organise. Some people

find it easier to make notes when using printed resources: pages can be bookmarked, sections highlighted, and marginal notes can be made. With print-based material, some people find it easier to pace themselves and keep on target because they can skim forward to see what's coming next and how much work there is to do. But print is a very 'flat' medium – even with good-quality diagrams – and it also tends to impose a linear structure on the way people work through it. This may not suit everyone's learning style.

It is possible that you have experienced many of these benefits and drawbacks yourself as you've worked through Block 2, and that you've found others not listed above. You may be perfectly comfortable with both computer- and print-based materials. On the other hand, you may have some quite strong views on which medium you prefer. It will be an advantage to you if you can develop strategies that help you to get the best out of both media. For example, if you have found it difficult to get access to a computer at times that are convenient for you, you might be able to reorganise your study patterns to solve this problem. If you find animations particularly helpful and find that print resources don't provide you with an equivalent insight, you could try searching the Web. (Try entering 'RFID animation' as a Google search term and see what comes up.)

Activity 34 (exploratory)

Review the influence of the different learning media on your learning experience as you worked through Block 2. Complete a journal entry that answers the questions below, but feel free to add other relevant comments.

(a) What did you most like and most dislike about the computer-based learning materials?

(b) What did you most like and most dislike about the print-based learning materials?

(c) What have you discovered about your own learning preferences as a result of using the different media in Block 2?

(d) What strategies could you adopt to help you get the best out of the different learning media you are likely to meet in later parts of the course?

Comment

It would be a good idea to write another journal entry reflecting on your study of Block 2 as a whole. You could note any parts of the block which you need to return to later, or any skills which you need to work on.

ANSWERS TO SELF-ASSESSMENT QUESTIONS

Activity 7

Networked devices need protocols when communicating with each other to:

- establish a common language;
- control use of the communication link.

Activity 8

(a) $34\ 200 = 3.42 \times 10^4$

(b) $5\ 340\ 000\ 000 = 5.34 \times 10^9$

(c) $690 = 6.9 \times 10^2$

(d) $69 = 6.9 \times 10^1$

Activity 10

1   The frequency of an electromagnetic wave is measured in units of Hertz.

2   An electromagnetic wave with a frequency of 10^8 Hz lies within the band of frequencies known as radio waves.

3   'Modulation' is the term given to the process of modifying a carrier to represent data.

4   Energy from a signal is absorbed by the transmission medium. This weakens the signal.

Activity 11

(a) 3.5×10^6

(b) 2×10^3

(c) 4.31×10^{11}

(d) 3.95×10^6

Activity 12

1   The term often used to describe devices connected to a wired network is 'node'.

2   Every node is assigned a MAC address. It is a number that uniquely identifies each node on a local area network.

3   A repeater takes a weak signal and regenerates it before passing it on.

4   A switch or bridge separates a network into segments and only passes on frames that are intended for an adjacent segment or that need to be routed through it. This means that nodes aren't competing with every other node for access to the network.

Activity 16

Radio waves occupy the portion of the electromagnetic spectrum lying between about 10^3 Hz (1 kHz) and 10^{10} Hz (10 GHz)

Activity 18

(a) The statement is false. In ad hoc mode, the WiFi network is isolated from any other network.

(b) The statement is false. Data rate is affected by distance from the AP and the presence of any physical barriers, so stations connected to a WiFi infrastructure network are likely to achieve different data rates.

(c) The statement is true. Every WiFi station requires a MAC address so that it can be uniquely identified within the network.

(d) The statement is false. Throughput is a term that describes the effective message data rate. This is lower than the maximum data rate because some of the data capacity is used by protocol overheads and management data.

Activity 19

1   The statement is false. Bluetooth devices communicate using radio waves.

2   The statement is true. The Bluetooth standard is within the IEEE 802.15 family of standards for wireless PANs. Bluetooth has a maximum range of about 10 m so is unsuitable for wider geographical areas.

3   The statement is false. Bluetooth devices need a MAC address to provide them with a network identity.

4   The statement is true. The upper limit on the number of devices that can communicate in a piconet is eight, but piconets can be joined together to form larger networks.

Activity 20

The completed Table 2 is shown below as Table 4.

Table 4   Comparison of WiFi IEEE 802.11g and Bluetooth

Characteristic	WiFi	Bluetooth
How transmitted	wireless in ISM band	wireless in ISM band
Equipment needed	NIC and possibly access point	Bluetooth-enabled microchip
Maximum data rate	54 Mpbs	1 Mbps
Approximate maximum throughput	30 Mbps	721 kbps
Methods for sharing the medium	protocols for sharing	controlled by master unit
Optimum operating range	Up to 30 m	Less than 10 m
Standards family	IEEE 802.11	IEEE 802.15
Network structure	ad hoc or infrastructure	piconet or scatternet
Number of nodes supported	depends on equipment manufacturer but limited by practical data rate	8 per piconet but more when piconets connected into a scatternet

Activity 21

My answer is given below. You will almost certainly have used different words from me to describe the main theme, but I hope we are in broad agreement over the topic of each paragraph.

Paragraph 1	The need for Bluetooth.
Paragraph 2	Bluetooth standard – when developed and the parties involved.
Paragraph 3	Transmission technology – frequency used and equipment needed.
Paragraph 4	Piconets.
Paragraph 5	Scatternets.
Paragraph 6	Range and data rate.

Activity 23

Although the sample was a fairly short piece of text I felt that it would divide well into three separate paragraphs – one for each of the topics identified in the first three of the set of bullet points immediately before Activity 23.

Next I looked at ordering, deciding that the points that provided a general introduction to the technologies should come first. The explanation about the different interfaces provided some of the background to the different uses, so I put that next. I also made sure that I defined the meaning of each abbreviation as I used it (but if I used the abbreviation later in the document I didn't repeat the definition).

Here is my attempt:

> WiFi and Bluetooth are technologies that provide a means of transmitting data wirelessly between devices. Both use the 2.4 GHz industrial, scientific and medical (ISM) radio frequency band and both are defined by a set of standards produced by the Institute of Electrical and Electronics Engineers (IEEE).
>
> All devices need some kind of network interface to enable them to transmit and receive signals. WiFi uses a network interface card (NIC) but Bluetooth uses a small low-power microchip which is better suited for incorporation into small devices.
>
> WiFi is able to transmit data up to 10 times faster than Bluetooth, and has a greater range – typically 30 m compared to 10 m for Bluetooth. This makes it more suitable for use in local area networks where it can be used as an alternative to a wired network. Bluetooth, on the other hand, is generally used for short-range communication between ICT devices such as computers, printers, keyboards and personal digital assistants (PDAs) where it eliminates the need for connecting cables.

Activity 27

$$20 \text{ ms} = \frac{20}{1000} \text{ s} = 0.02 \text{ s}$$

$$\frac{0.02}{0.5} \times 100 = 4\% \text{ duty cycle}$$

Activity 31

Here is my attempt:

> There are two main types of RFID tag – active tags, which carry their own battery power source, and passive tags, which draw their power from the RFID reader. Active tags tend to be larger, heavier and more expensive than passive tags, but they also tend to have a larger memory size (typically 1 Mbyte) and a longer read range (about 100 feet). The lifespan of an active tag is limited to 10 years, but passive tags can have an unlimited lifespan. However, the performance capability of passive tags is lower as they have a shorter read range (no more than 10 feet), lower memory size (typically 32 to 128 bits), and typically read-only functions. Passive tags also require higher-powered readers.

REFERENCES

AIM (n.d.) *What is Radio Frequency Identity (RFID)?* [online] Association for Automatic Identification and Mobility. Available from http://www.aimglobal.org/technologies/rfid/what_is_rfid.asp [Accessed 24 November 2004]

Gates, W.H. (1996) *The Road Ahead*, England, Penguin Books Ltd., pp. 250–1.

Hecht, J. (2004) 'Casinos lead the chip revolution'. *The New Scientist*, vol. 181, no. 2429, p. 21.

Hecht, B. and Hecht, F. (2004) *Radio ID Tags for US Drugs*. MedicineNet.com, [online]. Available from http://www.medicinenet.com/script/main/art.asp?articlekey = 40579 [Accessed 09 December 2004].

Information Week (2004) *RFID to Fight Counterfeiting of Viagra, Pain Killing Drug* Information Week 15 November [online]. Available from http://www.informationweek.com/story/showArticle.jhtml?articleID = 52601667 [Accessed 03 December 2004]

Losowsky, A. (2004) *I've got you under my skin,* The Guardian, 10 June, p. 21.

Palmer, M. (October 2004) *The Hidden Secret of the 5 Cent RFID Tag* [online], Software Development Times. Available from http://www.sdtimes.com/opinions/guestview_111.htm [Accessed 24 November 2004]

RFID News (2004) *RFID-enabled licence plates to identify UK vehicles* [online] RFID News, 10 June. Available from (http://www.rfidnews.org/news/2004/06/10/rfidenabled-license-plates-to-identify-uk-vehicles/ [Accessed 07 December 2004]

Shepherd D. (2003) *Networked Microsensors and the End of the World as We Know It.* IEEE Technology and Society Magazine, Spring, p. 16.

SkyeTek Inc. (2004) *SkyeTek Announces World's Smallest RFID Reader* [online], SkyeTek Inc., 14 January. Available from http://www.skyetek.com/article_m1_mini.html [Accessed 09 December 2004]

The Mannings Group. (n.d.) *How RFID Works* [online]. Available from http://www.iaid.com/acatalog/The_Mannings_Group_How_RFID_Works_32.html [Accessed 24 November 2004]

Williams, M. (2003) *Hitachi develops RFID chip for bank notes, documents* [online], Computerworld, 02 September. Available from http://www.computerworld.com/mobiletopics/mobile/story/0,10801,84543,00.html [Accessed 09 December 2004]

Young, K. (2004) *Shelf life.* The Guardian, 11 November, p. 16.

ACKNOWLEDGEMENTS

Grateful acknowledgement is made to the following sources for permission to reproduce material within this product.

Text

Page 90: Shepherd D. (2003), 'Networked Microsensors and the End of the World As We Know IT' ', *IEEE Technology and Society Magazine*, © 2003 IEEE.

Figures

Figure 22: © 2004 Google

Figure 23: © 2004 Google

APPENDIX 1

Networked Microsensors and the End of the World As We Know It

Shepherd, D.

Strategic Analysis Inc., Arlington, VA, USA; *This paper appears in:* **Technology and Society Magazine, IEEE**

Publication Date: Spring 2003

On page(s): 16–22

Volume: 22, Issue: 1

ISSN: 0278-0097

INSPEC Accession Number: 7556263

Abstract

Microsensors promise to bring people into closer contact with computers and, in the process, change society significantly. The author examines the impact of sensors on four areas: industrial manufacturing, military operations, personal health, and individual freedoms.

Index Terms

microsensors   social aspects of automation   technological forecasting   individual freedoms   industrial manufacturing   microsensors   military operations   networked sensors

Appendix 2

Microsensors promise to bring people into closer contact with computers and, in the process, change society significantly (and not necessarily for the better). Sensors and actuators link the world of events, tangible things, and organic creatures with the electronic world of computers, processors, and storage devices. Sensors accomplish this by integrating analog sensing with digital processing into a more efficient network where electronic fingers and tendrils pervade our lives and send signals to powerful databases and processors. Collaboration among the sensors – each of which will be a tiny computer (albeit comparatively low power and poor performance) – will enable real-time adaptation to environmental and user conditions and ensure that the whole becomes greater than the sum of the parts. Networked sensors will be remarkably responsive because of the quantity and quality (such as timeliness) of information provided to processors. The size of sensors and actuators will decrease to the point that actuators eventually will be small enough to course through individuals' bloodstreams and dispense medicine according to signals from similarly sized sensors. In some cases the sensors themselves will be organic elements of the body, sensing conditions and perhaps reporting to processors within the body or outside of it[1].

At this early stage of technological development, however, most people have not contemplated the ramifications of a society filled with sensors [2], [3]. One view of the future is provided by the founders of Ember Corporation, who envision a future when "every vine in a vineyard reports sunlight, temperature, and moisture every hour of the day, [when] every city street lamp monitors the passage of each bus" and relays information ahead to waiting passengers[2]. In other words, for the first time people will be able to monitor and control almost all aspects of their environment – including, potentially, other people. The social implications of this shift to integrated sensing and processing are enormous and varied, and probably are not entirely welcome to even the most enthusiastic technology proponent. Following are discussions examining the impact of sensors on four areas: industrial manufacturing, military operations, personal health, and individual freedoms [4].

Industrial Applications

Sensors already play an important role in industry. For several decades sensors without many internal smarts have been placed on or in machines to monitor wear, heat, lubrication levels, or similar information. In more recent years, though, with the diminishing size of the sensors and increasing power of computers and networks, industry experts have realized the value that sensors can add to a manufacturing or monitoring effort. Sensors have become "smart," or imbued with the capability to read data faster, process and manipulate it in more ways, and transmit it to multiple destinations for display, storage, or further processing. And with the rise of the networked, intelligent factory, the use of sensors has blossomed. For example, the

"Buyer's Guide 2002," produced by *Sensors*, a trade publication in existence for 18 years, lists 116 physical properties sensed, 79 technologies used in making and employing sensors, and more than 1900 suppliers, manufacturers, and solutions providers. *Sensors* itself has almost 80 000 paid subscribers and, among many related sections, has a feature section titled, "Putting Sensors to Work," devoted to sensors' role in industry[3].

The Institute for Electrical and Electronics Engineers (IEEE) is facilitating the implementation of sensors in industry. Until a few years ago there was no standard method of connecting sensors to networks; manufacturers produced what clients needed, or as clients or applications demanded. This resulted in a hodgepodge of sensors, fieldbus hardware, and interface software – a technological tower of Babel. Industry experts realized that for sensors to gain acceptance, let alone widespread use, interfaces and connections would have to be standardized. As a result, the IEEE Instrumentation and Measurement Society and the National Institute for Standards and Technology (NIST) launched the P1451 Smart Transducer Interface Standard to standardize sensors for use in industry in a "plug-and-play" fashion. This is intended to unscramble the assortment of technologies and ideas about connecting sensors to processors and networks. The latest version of the standard, 1451.2, calls for an electronic data sheet in sensor modules to ensure proper data formatting, and a digital interface to enable processors and networks to access the data sheet and to set actuators [5]–[7]. IEEE is also sponsoring a working group around the emerging standard for personal area networks (PANs), 802.15. Personal area networks are defined to have a radius of 5 to 10 m, a relatively tiny range well suited to deployment of multiple microsensors that blanket an area and connect in a mesh topology to provide redundancy and eliminate single points of failure. Like the Bluetooth concept of short-range wireless devices to eliminate wiring and facilitate flexibility, 802.15 promises to usher in an era of multiple devices interconnected using short-range links.

> ## At this early stage of technological development, most people have not contemplated the ramifications of a society filled with sensors.

This shift to more sensors, wired into factories and wireless in meshes, means that more goods can be produced in an automated fashion to exacting standards, thus increasing efficiency and decreasing waste. It also means that the goods produced by the factories can be instrumented to report machinery and product status in real time for use by the internal operations of the machine or equipment or for later use as conditions or users warrant. Similar sensors are currently used in automobiles to read pollution levels in the exhaust system as the engine runs, and to sense deceleration for use by airbag deployment triggers. In addition, sensors and actuators help to extend the life of plant equipment by enabling better diagnostic capabilities and by enabling condition-based maintenance for more consistent and tailored upkeep. Plus, not only are engineers putting sensors in the equipment built in shops and factories, designers are also building sensors such as strain gauges, accelerometers, and velocity sensors directly into the frames of buildings to detect structural damage and connecting them wirelessly to reduce the amount of hardware required. These embedded sensors report on the structural integrity and strength of the building itself and report the information either locally or to remote locations using the Internet. The end result of the employment of sensors, especially smart sensors, is a dynamic system of feedback and control that can sense conditions at the time of use, adapt to those conditions, and provide data for later processing. This system allows analysis of real-time data with the goal of producing smarter systems that can react to changes at a lightning pace [8]–[11].

BIOLOGICAL APPLICATIONS

Microsensors can also provide considerable benefits in the biomedical field for use during peacetime, wartime, or during the large gray zone between the two. For example, sensors can be used to help a person fighting infection determine medication levels or to provide continual readings on vital signs. In agriculture, the monitoring of short-term changes in fertilizer and pesticide levels or the long-term monitoring of moisture can be done using networks of wireless sensors. Especially given the current political climate, sensors that detect biological or chemical toxins and provide early warning of attacks or outbreaks can be of a great service to society. Research is under way on both inorganic sensors and organic, biological sensors that read the content levels of toxic substances and report the results over traditional wireless networks. Researchers are also looking to develop portable, automatic remote-sensing systems that can rapidly detect and diagnose biological agents. One futuristic application is sensors worn like wristwatches to provide individual sensing of chemical or biological agents. At the moment these systems are hardly portable and do not work in distributed, collaborative fashions, although the goal is to enable networked and distributed processing in the biological arena [12], [13].

While current systems are critical in cases of radiation leaks or disease contamination, the ultimate goal in sensors is to detect from within. In these cases, rather than tiny inorganic machines and computers, biological organisms

would do the sensing. Organic sensors offer the attraction of integrating with the body rather than being seen as foreign, and of using power sources the body already employs. Detectors currently under development include biological tissue-based systems that measure the responses of live cells to foreign agents or toxins, those that use test molecules to detect DNA sequences or proteins, and chemical mass-spectroscopy systems that compare the DNA fingerprint or amino-acid sequence of sample agents to known bioagents or molecules [14]. Researchers in the Tissue-Based Biosensor Program at the Defense Advanced Research Projects Agency (DARPA) are investigating ways to make biosensors to detect biological agents and toxins, to assess human health risks from biotoxins, and to enhance cellular performance for agent detection and increased longevity and biocompatibility. Issues in the construction of biosensors include determination of cell-nutrient requirements, hydrodynamics and efficient transportation of nutrients and wastes, spatial arrangements of cells within a matrix, and the signal processing of electrical, optical, mechanical or other outputs from cells. Researchers are also studying detection dynamics, user interfaces, and cellular signaling for event detection and reporting [15]. However, today few of these systems are small, robust, fast, and reliable enough to qualify as microsensors except in the size of their targets. The goal is to reduce sensor size so that the sensors can be implanted in the human body and transmit such signals as chemical levels over periods of time as long as years or decades. Sensors and actuators should be able to stream through the body, dispatching medication or providing messages alerting people to the conditions of their internal workings. Applications currently under research include health monitoring (such as glucose levels and organ conditions), cancer detection, and artificial eyesight. In the case of the artificial retina, a 10x10 grid of sensors is micromachined and attached to an aluminum probe, which is then covered in a biologically inert substance. This sensor would then placed directly on the non-functional human retina, where it would produce an electrical signal resulting from light inputs. These inputs are would then be converted to a chemical signal by the tissue of the retina for eventual transmission to the brain via the optic nerve. At this time more work needs to be done on the integration of tissues with synthetic materials and the processing of the signals sent by the sensors so that the image can be more easily understood by the brain [14, p. 305], [16].

Implantable, organic biosensors are still several years away, and networks of biosensors even further. The same engineering and system-design challenges found in traditional sensor and wireless communication areas can be found in the arena of biomedical sensors, but are magnified. Low-power operation, robust and continuous operation in harsh environments, noise and topological considerations, size and weight constraints, low probabilities of detection and high probabilities of false alarms, and limited processing power all apply. The sensors will have to be robust enough to operate for years, or cheap and plentiful enough to be replaced easily. Power remains a critical issue. Work is ongoing on powering the sensors using the body itself, whether the power is derived from the motion of walking or the body's heat. And, of course, all electromechanical devices give off energy in the form of heat; how will the

sensors' heat and "exhaust emissions" affect the body? Despite these challenges the body remains a fertile area for sensor usage, and researchers continue to improve sensors and actuators each day with the goal of fully integrating them into human beings [17], [18].

MILITARY APPLICATIONS

Sensors intended for military use are distinguished not only by their applications, but also by the implications for their failure, when large numbers of lives are at stake [19]. One way to increase the chance of mission success is to keep commanders as informed as possible about enemy and friendly movements and force compositions. As a result, the military mission that benefits perhaps most from the use of sensors is reconnaissance, both long range and short range. Reconnaissance missions provide intelligence about battle spaces, or the placement and movements of friendly and enemy units; as well as about civilian personnel, the lay of the land, and other noncombatant factors. Sensors provide the raw information, which can be processed by humans or machines to eventually become useful intelligence. However, because the battlefield environment is so stressful and the penalties for failure so high, sensor systems must be designed to fuse data or perform intelligent processing and filtering to ensure that users are not inundated with too much information – or (of course) misinformation. Another mission in which sensors could benefit the military is chemical and biological weapons detection. Since soldiers face the possibility of being attacked with chemical or biological weapons, it would make sense to issue sensors directly to the soldiers in the field. Aside from biological sensors, sensors useful to the military range from air-launched, long-range acoustic sensors, to sensors towed from ships, to short-range, multiple-modality, networked sensors for insertion by personnel or unmanned aerial vehicles (UAVs) [20], [21]. To maximize useful information, especially in the case of unattended ground sensors, networks are being built so that multiple sensors can act collaboratively, with readings from multiple modalities (such as acoustic, seismic, infrared, magnetic, and visual) fused to provide one coherent signal. Sensors useful to the military must be ruggedized and have redundant systems to ensure success. To maximize the likelihood that at least some useful information will be transmitted, sensor networks for the military should be built without single points of failure, in case that a single node malfunctions or is eliminated from the network. Furthermore, networks of microsensors deployed along the ground in military missions should be mobile to account for shifting battle lines or missions, while sensors deployed in and from aircraft must account for rapidly changing atmospheric conditions and large geographic area coverage. Mobile sensors must carry their own power sources. And it is preferable for the sensors to transmit few or low power signals to avoid detection by the enemy. All these factors mean that sensors for the military must be ruggedly built, power efficient, self-organizing (which adds additional processing and power requirements), and in the case of hand-deployed sensors, small and light enough to be carried by soldiers already burdened by weapons, food, and gear [22]–[24][4].

Algorithms and technologies currently under research provide promise for sensor effectiveness in military and civilian societies in the coming years. While the use of sensors is not widespread at this time, sensors loom large in Pentagon plans for the battlespace of the future[5]. Sensors can help lift the fog and uncertainty of the battlefield by providing multispectral information with a minimum loss of life. This improvement argues for their usage, even though the technology is not always advanced enough at this stage to provide reliable readings to troops whose lives are on the line. For this reason the military comprises both the best and the worst organization in society to employ sensors: the penalties for failure are high, yet the military has the organizational and disciplinary structure to deploy and utilize sensors successfully. Plus, the military has a mission for which sensors would be clearly applicable. As a result, the military should lead the way in sensor development and use but also conduct rigorous usage and testing in peacetime environments to ensure success if sensors are used in wartime.

SENSORS AND PERSONAL PRIVACY

Owing to its tight disciplinary hold on its personnel, the military escapes questions about the one area of sensor usage that perhaps most troubles civilian society: privacy. Sensors offer the capability of monitoring virtually everything using technologies such as cameras mounted on small, mobile platforms and long-range, multispectral sensors capable of "seeing" thermal, acoustic, magnetic, or other types of signatures. Coupled with massive databases, powerful search engines, and faster processors, today's sensors can register an image or signature and compare it to databases for analysis and recommended action.

The implications for society are harrowing. Societies along the lines of those discussed years ago in George Orwell's *1984* and Jeremy Bentham's *Panopticon* come to mind, with people cowed into submission by the threat of constant surveillance, real or implied. Will the diminishing size of sensors and the growing power of networks and processors mean that sensors will soon be everywhere? This statement implies a technological determinism that omits people as decision-makers [25], [26]. Especially given the current trends toward acceptance of technologies, the real question should be, "Will people permit sensors to pervade all aspects of their lives?" This development is not farfetched because sensors could be seen as an antidote to crime, and because people might be afraid to oppose those segments of society interested in sensors, such as powerful industrial manufacturers or the government. Plus, pressures to accept and employ sensors would surely become even more difficult to resist as sensors become more and more pervasive [27]–[33].

In this respect sensors do not add anything new to the arguments for or against monitoring and surveillance [34], [35]. Instead, sensors make existing surveillance simpler, cheaper, and more efficient. With their wireless connections, small size, light weight, and RF communications, microsensors can provide the technology needed to make electronic networks ever more

pervasive by enabling the final connections between the networks themselves and the subjects of their surveillance. In some respects this pervasiveness will be a welcome change. Remote and movable sensors can be placed at high-crime locations; infrared sensors can track personnel movements when no light is available; seismic sensors can be placed with valuable cargoes to monitor shifts in weight distribution. Sensors can extend people's eyes and ears, or present a threat of that occurring, which is often more effective than real, hidden monitoring. But this means a reduction in privacy. In effect, sensors provide the technology to erase privacy in every arena except perhaps the unexpressed thoughts of the human mind.

Indeed, while easing the minds of people performing surveillance, sensors contribute to unease of potential targets of surveillance, who could be almost anyone. By enabling remote monitoring or enabling watchers to escape notice while observing their subjects, sensors help to bring about a condition that violates personal autonomy and the principle that submission of information should be voluntary. One condition that has brought about an outcry is local governments' and police departments' use of cameras to photograph vehicles as they pass through intersections in order to catch drivers who run red lights. The American Civil Liberties Union (ACLU), which attempts to safeguard citizens' rights against unlawful or unwanted restrictions on personal liberties, has urged that this form of video surveillance be halted or delayed until privacy issues can be settled. And these arguments do not even account for troubles arising from the system's inability to accomplish its goal. Problems have arisen, such as issuing tickets to owners of cars when the owner of the automobile was not the speeding driver, or the improper use of information gained by intercepting radio frequency signals used for networked communications [36]. Will people use this and other forms of sensor technology only for benign purposes? The ACLU fears that a form of "mission creep" would occur in the use of technologies for surveillance. In other words, cameras intended to prevent traffic violations would soon be used for more intrusive ends, such as keeping databases on driver habits or watching pedestrian behavior, and would soon lead to the videotaping of all elements of society [37]–[39]. After all, while the United States has laws to prevent wiretapping and other forms of interception of voice communications using electronic media, these protections have not been expanded to include restrictions against other types of electronic monitoring. Because of sensors' small size and multiple ways of sensing the environment, the likelihood of sensors being used for other than benign reasons increases dramatically. Much as people knowledgeable in the use of the Internet feel that no information posted to or communicated via the Internet is private, sensors present the ominous condition that everything done or spoken in daily life will be open to scrutiny.

PROS AND CONS ABOUND

Is the role of sensors in society a foregone conclusion, especially given Americans' seemingly insatiable appetite for technological innovations [40]? The increasing processing power of computers, the connectivity provided

by wireless technologies, the diminishing size of electronic components, the possibilities of completely organic sensors; and most of all, people's desires to understand and control their environments all argue that people will embrace microsensors as another means of controlling their lives or bringing enjoyment into it.

Yet sensors can facilitate centralized control, or at a minimum the loss of individual privacy. Langdon Winner proposes that artifacts themselves have political qualities, that some technologies more than others facilitate certain forms of political government or control of populations [41]. In these cases, Winner says, we ought to know the technologies better and understand the consequences of adopting their use, since the implications of adopting the technologies might be vast or unfortunate. This would seem to be especially relevant in the case of microsensors. Ideally society will examine the new "calculus of privacy" brought about by sensors and other networked elements and wrestle with the disappearance of personal privacy [42][6]. Perhaps governments and private industry groups, such as IEEE, could facilitate a debate on the use of sensors to better prepare society for the changed environment and limited privacy of a future filled with sensors. However, given people's current willingness to permit technology into so many domains of their lives, the decision to permit the intrusion might already be made.

Especially in light of recent anthrax scares and the terrorist attacks of September 11, there is an urgent need to find solutions, including technical ones, to the presence of terrorists and the possibilities of homeland violence [43]. While sensors can help to attain these objectives, it is more likely that people will embrace sensors because sensors offer something that even the networked world of current information technologies cannot offer: the possibility of intimately connecting people and the environment to computers and controls. Historians of science and technology debate whether technology drives society or the reverse. In the case of sensors, technology and society drive each other, since sensors exist at the intersection of the two.

[NOTES]

[1]The microsensors considered in this article are designed to act collaboratively in large networks without each sensor itself having much intelligence. However, many researchers are working on smart sensors and sensor agents, or devices that have the processing power to make high-level decisions and exhibit human behavior. See [1].

[2]Ember Corporation, 1 Broadway 14th Floor, Cambridge, MA 02142 (www.ember.com). The startup company aims at the market for "extremely low-cost, wireless 'thing-to-thing' networks for countless embedded processors, sensors, and controls." Another manufacturer of low-cost, wireless microsensors is Crossbow Technologies (www.xbow.com).

[3]Recent articles in the "Putting Sensors to Work" section include Carl Smith and Robert Schneider, "The Color of Money: Using Magnetic Media Detection to Identify Currency" (November 2001) and David Aslin, "Monitoring Bearing and Gear Failure in Aircraft Gas Turbine Engines" (October 2001).

[4]One research program sponsored by the Department of Defense to research these problems is the Sensor Information Technology (SensIT) Program at the Defense Advanced Research Projects Agency. See [22].

[5]See, for example, the Expeditionary Pervasive Sensors Experimental Environment (EEE). A program intended to integrate multiple sensor types and platforms, the EEE is a multi-tiered, war fighter-centered architecture of numerous and heterogeneous battlespace sensors to support a more distributed, information-oriented style of warfare.

[6]On the issue of the looming elimination of personal privacy, see issues of *New York Times Magazine*, October 7, 2001 and April 14, 2002, devoted to the subject.

REFERENCES

[1] G. Allgood and W. Manges, "Sensor agents – When engineering emulates human behavior," *Sensors,* vol. 28, Aug. 2001.

[2] P. Saffo, "Sensors: The next wave of infotech innovation," *Institute for the Future 1997 Ten-Year Forecast*, pp. 115–122.

[3] *Embedded, Everywhere: A Research Agenda for Networked Systems of Embedded Computers,* Washington DC: National Academy Press, 2001.

[4] Alfred D. Chandler, Jr. and James Cortada, Eds, *A Nation Transformed by Information: How Information has Shaped the United States from Colonial Times to the Present*, New York: Oxford Univ. Press, 2000.

[5] B. Travis, "Sensors smarten up," *EDN Access*, Mar. 4, 1999.

[6] J. Montague, "Reaching up and out: Interface standards smarten up sensors, transducers," *Control Engineering*, Dec. 1999.

[7] R. N. Johnson, "Building plug-and-play networked smart transducers," *Sensors Mag.*, Oct. 1997.

[8] K. Mitchell, N. Dang, P. Liu, S. Rao, and H. Pottinger, "Web-controlled wireless network sensors for structural health monitoring," in *Proc. SPIE Int. Soc. for Optical Engineering*, 2001, p. 234.

[9] W. Manges *et al.*, "Intelligent wireless sensors for industrial manufacturing," *Sensors*, Apr. 2000.

[10] B. Jakoby, "Microacoustic sensors for automotive applications," in *2000 IEEE Ultrasonics Symp. Proc.*, 2000, pp. 453–460.

[11] B. Nickerson and R. Lally, "Development of a smart wireless networkable sensor for aircraft engine health management," in *2001 IEEE Aerospace Conf. Proc.,* vol. 7, 2001.

[12] *Opportunities in Biotechnology for Future Army Applications.* Washington, DC: National Academy Press, 2001, p. 17.

[13] C. Aston, "Biological warfare canaries," *IEEE Spectrum*, p. 37, Oct. 2001.

[14] K. G. Ong *et al.*, "Monitoring of bacterial growth using a wireless, remote query resonant-circuit sensor: Application to environmental sensing," *Biosensors and Bioelectronics,* vol. 16, p. 306, 2001.

[15] Tissue-Based Biosensor Program, Defense Advanced Research Projects Agency, DARPA/DSO, Arlington, VA.

[16] S. K. S. Gupta, L. Schwiebert, J. Weinmann, "Research challenges in wireless networks of biomedical sensors," in *Proc. Ann. Int. Conf. on Mobile Computing and Networking*, 2001, pp. 151–165.

[17] A. Rudolph and J. Reasor, "Cell and tissue based technologies for environmental detection and medical diagnosis," *Biosensors and Bioelectronics*, vol. 16, pp. 429–430, 2001.

[18] *Opportunities in Biotechnology for Future Army Applications*, National Academy Press, 2001.

[19] K. Burger, "JFCOM seeks faster acquisition of anti-terrorist 'tools'," *Jane's Defence Weekly*, Oct. 24, 2001.

[20] M. Hewish, "Little brother is watching you," *International Defense Rev.,* vol. 34, no. 6, June 1, 2001.

[21] D. Fulgham, "Sensor networks key to defeating stealth," *Aviation Week & Space Technology*, vol. 137, no. 21, p. 30, Nov. 23, 1992.

[22] J. R. Wilson, "The incredible shrinking sensor," *Military & Aerospace Electronics*, vol. 13, no. 3, pp. 23–24, Mar 2002.

[23] B. E. Boser *et al.,* "Energy and performance considerations for smart dust," *Int. J. of Parallel Distributed System Networks*, vol. 4, no. 3, p. 121–133, 2001.

[24] A. Sindha and A.P. Chandrakasan, "Operating system and algorithmic techniques for scalable wireless sensor networks," in *Mobile Data Management Second Int. Conf. Proc.*, 2001, pp. 199–209.

[25] M. Roe Smith and L. Marx, Eds, *Does Technology Drive History? The Dilemma of Technological Determinism.* Cambridge, MA: M.I.T. Press, 1994, pp. 1–36.

[26] T. Hughes, "Technological momentum," in *Does Technology Drive History? The Dilemma of Technological Determinism*, M.R. Smith and L. Marx, Eds. Cambridge, MA: M.I.T. Press, pp. 101–114.

[27] J. Bentham, *Panopticon.* Dublin, 1787.

[28] G. Orwell, *1984.* London, U.K.: Harcourt Brace Jovanovich, 1949.

[29] B. Dority, "Big brother is watching!" *The Humanist*, pp. 12–13, May/June 2001.

[30] A. Etzioni, *The Limits of Privacy.* New York, NY: Basic, 1999, pp. 2, 10.

[31] G. T. Marx, "Ethics for the new surveillance," *Information Society*, vol. 14, pp. 176, 182, Jul.–Sept. 1998.

[32] A. Moore, "Intangible property: Privacy, power, and information control," *American Philosophical Quart.*, vol. 35, no. 4, pp. 373–374, Oct. 1998.

[33] J. Rosen, "Being watched," *New York Times Mag.*, p. 43, Oct. 7, 2001.

[34] A. Moore, "Employee monitoring and computer technology: Evaluative surveillance vs. privacy," *Business Ethics Quart.*, vol. 10, no. 3, July 2000.

[35] L. Hartman, "Technology and ethics: Privacy in the workplace," *Business and Society Rev.*, vol. 106, no. 1, Spr. 2001.

[36] J. Schwartz, "Nanny-cam may leave a home exposed," *New York Times*, Apr. 14, 2002, p. 1.

[37] E. Hendricks, T. Hayden, J. Novik, *Your Right to Privacy: A Basic Guide to Legal Rights in an Information Society.* Carbondale, IL: Southern Illinois Univ. Press, 1990.

[38] "Privacy in America: Electronic monitoring," ACLU in Brief Website, http://www.aclu.org/library/pbr2.html

[39] "ACLU urges halt to use of red-light cameras until privacy and fairness issues are addressed," American Civil Liberties Union press release, Aug. 23, 2001.

[40] "Fewer buffaloes, livelier democracy: Technology is shaking up culture, society and politics, mostly for the better," *Economist* editorial, 2001.

[41] D. MacKenzie and J. Wajcman, Eds, *The Social Shaping of Technology: How the Refrigerator Got its Hum.* Philadelphia, PA: Open University Press, 1985, p. 37.

[42] *Embedded, Everywhere: A Research Agenda for Networked Systems of Embedded Computers.* Washington, DC: National Academy Press, 2001, p. 182.

[43] "Technology vs. terror," *Technology Rev.*, Dec. 2001.